Understanding the Natural World

Science Today

William J. Reville

IRISH TIMES BOOKS

First published 1999 by The Irish Times Ltd.
10–16 D'Olier Street, Dublin 2 Ireland

© William J. Reville 1999

Distribution: Irish Times General Services
Telephone (01) 679 2022 ext. 8271
Fax (01) 671 8446
email itbooks@irish-times.ie

2 4 6 8 10 9 7 5 3 1

ISBN 0 907011 27 6

Editorial & design direction: Brenda McNiff
Index: Stephanie Dagg
Cover design: Terry Foley
Typesetting and design: A. & A. Farmar
Printed by Betaprint, Dublin, Ireland

Contents

Foreword

Although numerous surveys have shown that knowledge of science is low amongst the general public, there is a general underlying public appreciation of the importance of science in the modern world. In my experience, there is a widespread latent interest in science that can easily be pricked into life by readily digestible scientific information. Of course there is nothing very surprising in this: as Aristotle said 'All men, by their very nature, feel the urge to know'. People delight in understanding the natural world.

The weekly 'Science Today' column in *The Irish Times* began in January 1995. The public response to the column was very positive right from the start and I have been greatly heartened by the volume and tone of the correspondence I have received. Many readers have suggested that I should gather a collection of my articles into book form and this publication is a response to that prompting.

The book is divided into sections, as follows: The Universe at Large; The Solar System and the Earth; Some laws of Physics; The Origin of Life and The Theory of Evolution; Modern Genetics; Medicine and Disease; Diet, Nutrition and Lifestyle; the Environment; Science and Religion.

The 'Science Today' column is aimed at the general reading public and assumes little or no knowledge of science. Each article aims to provide a brief overview of the particular topic, capable of standing alone and not dependent for its understanding on material presented in other articles. I hope also that the articles are sufficiently rigorous to interest scientists who are not specialists in the particular topic.

Thanks are due in *The Irish Times* to Conor Brady, Editor, for his generous encouragement of my efforts; Gerry Smyth, Managing Editor, with whom I liaised concerning the column for a couple of years, and

Dick Ahlstrom, Science Editor, who is eminently cool and pleasant to work with.

I worked closely with Brenda McNiff, General Services Manager, in producing the book and I thank Brenda for the considerable effort she expended and for her general good humour in guiding the project to completion.

Finally, my thanks to Aisling Ní Mhurchú, my secretary at University College Cork, who did all the word-processing of the manuscript for this book and who also helped me in numerous other ways to get the book together.

William J. Reville
September 1999

Acknowledgements

The author and publishers wish to thank the following for allowing the reproduction of illustrations:

Front cover:

Light spectrum: From *The Ascent of Man* by J. Bronowski (1976). Reproduced by kind permission of BBC Educational Publications Photographer, Peter Brierly.

Earth seen from the moon: NASA.

Dolly and Bonnie: By kind permission of Ian Wilmutt and The Roslin Institute. Photographer, Roddy Fields.

Back cover:

The Great Nebula M42 in Orion (taken by 200 inch telescope on Mount Palomar): By kind permission of BBC Educational Publications and The University of Newcastle-upon-Tyne.

Endpapers:

A fossil skeleton of a flying reptile, a pterosaur of the species *Pterodactylus elegans*. It lived 135 million years ago. Taken from *Fossils and the History of Life* by Gaylord Simpson (Scientific American Books, W. H. Freeman and Co., 1983) Photographer, Fritz Goro.

Illustrations in the text:

Pages 43, 50: Taken from *Reverse Time Travel* by Barry Chapman (Cassell, 1995). Reproduced by kind permission of Cassell plc.

Page 55: Taken from *Schrödinger's Kittens and the Search for Reality* by John Gribbin (Weidenfeld and Nicolson, 1995). By kind permission of John Gribbin and Weidenfeld and Nicolson.

Page 74: NASA

Page 77: Taken from *Theories of Everything* by John Barrow (Clarendon Press, 1991). By kind permission of John Barrow and Clarendon Press.

Page 80: Negative transparency no. 324393. Photographer, Roland T.

Bird. Reproduced courtesy of the Dept. of Library Services, American Museum of Natural History.

Page 125: Taken from *Genetic Fingerprinting* by Pauline Lowrie and Susan Wells (*Inside Science* No. 52, *New Scientist*, 16 November 1991). Diagram by Peter Gardiner. Reproduced by kind permission of *New Scientist*.

Page 195: Taken from 'Are the stray 60HZ electromagnetic fields associated with the distribution and use of electrical power a significant cause of cancer?' by J. D. Jackson (*Proceedings of National Academy of Science*, USA, Volume 89, pp. 3508–10, 1992). Reproduced by kind permission of J. D. Jackson and Proceedings of National Academy of Science.

Colour section

Figure 1: The Granger Collection

Figures 2,3 NASA

Figure 4: Taken from *The Family Encyclopaedia of Natural History*. Editor Rosalind Carreck (Windward, 1982). By kind permission of Instituto Geografica de Augustini, Italy.

Figure 5: Taken from *Biology: The Unity and Diversity of Life*, 5th edition, by C. Starr and R. Taggart © 1989. Reprinted with permission of Brooks/Cole Publishing, a division of Thomas Learning. Fax 800 730-2215.

Figure 6: Reproduced by kind permission of Professor Ian Wilmutt and The Roslin Institute. Photographer, Roddy Fields.

Figure 7: Taken from: *Natural Sources of Ionising Radiation in Europe* Commission of the European Communities 1993

The Universe at Large

The Origin, Nature and Future of the Universe

For many people, the most interesting area in physics is cosmology—the study of the universe as a whole, including theories of its origin, evolution, large-scale structure and future. It would take a profound lack of imagination not to be engaged by these topics and, consequently, most people are familiar with the general idea that the universe is thought to have began in a titanic explosion called 'the Big Bang'. Big Bang Theory is currently in the ascendant in cosmology to describe, not only the origin, but many other features of the universe.

The earliest cosmological theories, dating back to 4,000 years BC, held that the Earth is at the centre of the universe and that the other heavenly bodies rotate around it. This position generally held until 1543 when Copernicus (1473–1543) proposed that the planets revolve in circular orbits around the Sun, which sits at the centre of the universe. Kepler (1571–1630) agreed with this view, but discovered that the planets move in elliptical orbits and at different speeds according to three laws (Kepler's Laws). Galileo (1564–1642) first observed the planets with a telescope and championed the Copernican model. Sir Isaac Newton (1642–1727) showed that Kepler's Laws could be derived from his own general laws of motion and gravitation—the laws of physics held sway in the heavens as well as on Earth.

The light-year is a unit of astronomical distance. Light travels at a speed of 186,000 miles per second, and a light-year is the distance it travels in one year. Our solar system is part of the Milky Way galaxy, which is estimated to be roughly 100,000 light-years in diameter. Our Sun is not stationary in the galaxy—it takes about 250 million years to travel once around the centre of the galaxy. The Milky Way galaxy contains about 200,000 million stars.

There are about one hundred billion other galaxies in the universe beyond our Milky Way. The nearest spiral galaxy to us is the Andromeda galaxy, 2.2 million light years away. In 1912, an American astronomer, Vesto Slipher, reported that the wavelength of light reaching us from distant galaxies is stretched out towards longer (red) wavelengths. This is called the red shift and it shows that most galaxies are receding from the Milky Way at a speed of several hundred kilometres per second. Another American astronomer, Edwin Hubble, found that the more remote the galaxy, the greater is its recession velocity. He formulated a law (Hubble's Law, 1929) which states that the recession velocity of a galaxy is proportional to its distance from us. The ratio of the recession velocity of a galaxy to its distance is called the Hubble constant, one of the most important numbers in cosmology. Efforts are ongoing to get more and more reliable estimates of this constant.

Looking out into space from Earth we can see all other galaxies, in all directions, moving away from us. Does this mean that our galaxy is at the centre of the universe? No. The true situation is more accurately visualised by thinking of a balloon with evenly spaced dots painted on it to represent the galaxies. As the balloon is inflated, an observer on any spot will see all the other spots moving away, just as observers on Earth see all galaxies receding from the Milky Way. The universe is expanding like a balloon.

Albert Einstein in 1917 put forward a model of the universe based on his new general theory of relativity. According to his model, the universe could not be static, but must be either contracting or expanding. The expansion of the universe had not yet been observed. Einstein refused to believe the conclusions inherent in his own equations and he introduced a 'cosmological constant' into them to produce a static universe. He thus missed the chance to predict the expansion of the universe. He later declared this to be 'the greatest mistake of my life'.

Imagine that the behaviour of the universe from the very beginning was recorded on film. The camera at present observes the universe expanding in all directions. But if you run the film backwards, the universe will be seen to get smaller and smaller, until eventually it is reduced to an infinitely small and infinitely dense point. This is thought to be the origin of the universe. It is proposed that this point erupted in a titanic explosion about fifteen billion years ago. The extremely high density in the primeval point would cause the universe to expand rapidly. This was originally proposed by the Russian–American physicist George Gamow in 1948 and is called the Big Bang Theory of the origin of the universe.

It is now believed, proposed by Alan Guth, that right at the very start the universe expanded at an exponential rate (inflation). During this phase, which lasted a split second, the size of the universe grew from 10^{20} times smaller than a proton to about the size of a grapefruit. Inflation then stopped and the universe continued to expand at a steady rate into the universe we have today.

Gamow proposed that the various elements observed today in the universe were formed within the first minutes of the Big Bang when the extremely high temperature and density fused subatomic particles into the chemical elements. It is now believed that hydrogen and helium were the main products of the Big Bang, with the heavier elements formed later in the stars. As the universe expanded, the hydrogen and helium cooled and condensed into stars and galaxies. This theory explains the basis for the expanding universe and for Hubble's Law.

The electromagnetic radiation energy released in the Big Bang was initially at a very high temperature but, as the universe expanded, it cooled down. This radiation should now have a temperature of about three degrees above absolute zero. This background relic microwave radiation was discovered in 1965 and provides important evidence in support of the Big Bang Theory. In 1992 tiny ripples were found in this otherwise smooth background radiation. The ripples indicate the early existence of clusters of matter, from which the first galaxies formed.

Will the universe continue to expand forever? This depends on the average density of matter in the universe. If the density is below a certain critical value, the gravitational attraction between the galaxies will not be great enough to eventually reverse the expansion, which will go on forever. If the density exceeds the critical value (estimated at 5×10^{-30} grams per cubic centimetre), the expansion will eventually be halted and contraction will set in. This would end in the gravitational collapse of the whole universe. If that happened, perhaps the universe would explode again, having reached an infinitely small dense point, later to collapse again, and so on forever.

Astronomers do not yet know accurately how much mass is in the universe. Ninety per cent, and more, of the mass in the universe, the so-called 'dark matter', can only be inferred to be present, since it is undetectable directly by current measuring apparatus. Until this dark matter has been accurately measured and characterised, the question of whether the universe will continue to expand forever or end up in 'the big crunch' will remain unanswered.

'What is the Stars?'

Mankind has been fascinated by the stars since ancient times. Ever eager to find order and pattern in nature, observers drew imaginary lines between stars to form outlines of familiar things like ploughs, bears and bulls. However, it was not until the last few hundred years, and particularly this century, that real progress was made in understanding the heavens. In a remarkable chapter of twentieth-century science, astronomers have worked out the main details of how stars are born, live their lives and die—stellar evolution.

Because stars live very long lives (billions of years), it is not possible to see the birth, lifespan and death of an individual star. However, when astronomers look at the sky, they see different stars at different stages of life and they can therefore piece together the full life-story of an individual star.

The universe is filled with a very dilute gas and small particles of dust. The gas is mostly hydrogen, with a small amount of helium. Here and there the gas and dust clump together to form interstellar gas clouds. Gravitational attraction causes the gas cloud to contract, making it denser, with the centre densest of all. At the centre, individual clumps form, and the temperature in the middle of each clump rises to an incredible ten million degrees Centigrade. Nuclear fusion reactions start at this temperature—hydrogen is converted into helium and huge amounts of energy are released, causing the clump to shine. This is how a star is born.

As the gas clump condenses to form a star, the central part condenses quickly, while the outer parts fall inwards more slowly. The condensing clump rotates and spins more quickly as the outer parts fall inwards. This causes the infalling gas/dust to form a disc around the central star. The material within the disc eventually forms planets that orbit the new star.

The mass of a star is fixed at birth and this mass determines the subsequent history of the star, i.e. how long it will live and how it will die. Our Sun is a typical star and it is convenient to use it as a standard when stating the mass of any other star. The mass of newborn stars covers a wide range, from 0.07 to 100 Suns.

The bigger a star, the hotter its centre, the faster its nuclear reactions run, the hotter its surface and the shorter its life. Our Sun has a surface temperature of 6,000°C. Heavyweight stars can shine as brightly as 100,000 Suns, with a surface temperature of 30,000°C. The mass of a star also determines how long it lives. Very massive stars quickly use up their hydrogen fuel, whereas very small stars, although having much smaller fuel supplies, burn the hydrogen slowly and live for a much longer time.

When a star is fusing its hydrogen into helium and burning brightly, it is said to be in its main sequence. Our Sun will spend about ten billion years as a main sequence star. A very massive star might survive only a thousandth of this time, while a very light star might live one hundred times longer than our Sun.

Smaller stars die in a different manner from the most massive stars. When the hydrogen at the core of a star like our Sun is used up, nuclear reactions still proceed in a thin shell surrounding the core. These reactions produce more energy than before and this pushes out, swelling the outer parts of the star. As these outer layers cool, they radiate a red colour. The star has become a 'red giant', about one hundred times its original size.

The outer regions of the red giant comprise a very thin gas. Eventually this outer gas drifts away into space leaving just a tiny, very hot, dense core which glows white hot—a 'white dwarf'. The white dwarf gradually cools down (it is generating no energy) and slowly fades from sight.

Our Sun was born five billion years ago. It has enough hydrogen to continue in main sequence for another five billion years, then it will swell into a red giant. It will engulf Mercury, then Venus. It will boil away the oceans on Earth before engulfing the planet altogether. Eventually it will shrink back to a white dwarf, around which the charred remnants of the planets will revolve.

Heavyweight stars end their lives more dramatically than the lighter stars. When the hydrogen in the core has all been converted into helium, the star expands into a giant. However, pressure and temperature in the core continue to rise until helium fuses to form carbon. Further increases in temperature and pressure cause carbon to change into heavier elements such as neon, silicon and iron. Eventually the star's centre becomes unstable and it collapses. The wave of collapse energy blows the star apart—a supernova.

The collapsing core of a supernova contracts into a super dense ball which is entirely composed of neutrons (a neutron is one of the main subatomic particles present in the nucleus of almost every atom). A neutron star is only about twenty-five kilometres in diameter and a piece the size of the roller ball in your ballpoint pen has a mass of a million tonnes. It would not be a good idea to land on a neutron star. The gravity is so strong that, if you did, you would be crushed and spread out in a layer over the surface one atom thick.

If the collapsing core of a supernova exceeds a certain mass (more than three Suns) it cannot end its days as a neutron star. Its gravity is so strong that it continues to condense until it reaches a single point with infinite density. This, and the space around it, is the black hole—'black' because no light can escape from it, and 'hole' because anything that goes into it can never escape again.

The blast from a supernova helps to start the process of star birth all over again. It compresses gas in space into clouds where gravity can get to work as already described. Also, by spewing out the heavier elements that it has formed, for example carbon and iron, it ensures that new stars will start out with slightly more of these heavier elements.

Smaller stars, like our Sun, are only capable of forging the lighter elements by nuclear reactions, but the massive stars that end their lives in supernova explosions can forge the full range of the elements. The Earth is rich in silicon, oxygen, aluminium and iron. Our bodies are rich in carbon, nitrogen and oxygen. Apart from hydrogen and helium, almost every atom on the Earth and in our bodies was bred in a star. We are, in our very essence, star dust.

Dust in Space

The regions between the stars in space are not empty. They contain a tenuous gas, mostly hydrogen, and grains of dust. In places the gas and dust congregate together to form interstellar clouds. If the clouds become dense enough they can give birth to new stars. Most interstellar space dust originates from old dying stars. Dust is also formed in our solar system when fragments are shed by collisions between asteroids and when debris is shed by comets.

My interest in cosmic dust was sparked recently when I read that creationists (who do not believe in evolution) claimed that the small amount of cosmic dust that has accumulated on the Moon proves that our solar system is much younger than is claimed by science. Neil Armstrong, they say, would have sunk into hundreds of feet of dust on a moon that was billions of years old, instead of leaving the neat footprints, that we all admired in awe, in dust a few inches deep. Of course, the depth of dust deposited is determined by multiplying the rate of deposition by the time of deposition. Astronomers explain that the creationists greatly exaggerate the rate of deposition.

Outside interstellar clouds, gas and dust are spread very thinly in space. A volume of interstellar space the size of a small packet of cigarettes would contain about six atoms of hydrogen gas, and one would have to search a volume the size of a large cathedral to find one dust grain. Individual grains are less than one millionth of a metre (a micrometre) in diameter. But, despite their tiny size and sparse distribution, interstellar distances are so great that light from faraway stars has to pass a vast number of dust grains in order to reach Earth.

Distance in space is measured in light-years, the distance light travels in one year (9.46 million million kilometres). Light reaching Earth from a star 3,000 light-years away is dimmed by half because of space dust between the star and Earth. Earth is about 30,000 light-years from the centre of the Milky Way galaxy, but because of the dimming of light by half every 3,000 light years, we can see little or nothing of the centre of the galaxy.

The dense concentration of dust in interstellar clouds essentially blocks out all light from stars beyond and the cloud appears as a dark silhouette in the heavens. A string of dark clouds can be seen in the northern hemisphere in the constellation Cygnus. These clouds extend over several thousand light-years and contain as much matter as one million Suns.

Light from the stars travels as a wave motion and there are many different wavelengths in the light. Matter can absorb light and different chemicals in matter absorb light preferentially at specific wavelengths. The light absorption characteristics of a piece of matter can therefore identify the chemical composition of the matter. Cosmic dust absorbs radiation at a wavelength of 9.7 micrometres, indicating that the majority of grains consist partly of silicates (compounds of silicon and oxygen with various metals), i.e. tiny chips of rock.

There is also evidence that cosmic grains contain other common elements, such as carbon, nitrogen and hydrogen. Along with oxygen these elements can form two kinds of molecule—ices and organic molecules. The ices consist of frozen water (H_2O), ammonia (NH_3), methane (CH_4), carbon monoxide (CO) and carbon dioxide (CO_2). Organic molecules tend to be large, with a backbone of carbon atoms to which are attached atoms of hydrogen, oxygen and nitrogen. Ultraviolet radiation starts reactions between the ice molecules to form a complicated mixture of organic molecules.

In addition to rocky grains, covered in sticky organic material and ice, cosmic dust also contains much smaller (0.01 micrometre) carbon grains. These make up only a few per cent of the total amount of space dust. The carbon occurs in two forms—amorphous (specks of soot) and hydrogenated (specks of soot with hydrogen atoms attached).

The largest and densest interstellar clouds are called molecular clouds because the gas atoms can join up to form simple molecules such as molecular hydrogen (H_2), formaldehyde (H_2CO) and ethanol

(C_2H_5OH). The gas and dust can become so dense that individual blobs can condense under their own gravity to form new stars, each surrounded by a disc of dust and gas that may form a system of planets. Our solar system was formed in this way about five billion years ago. The system was originally very dusty but most of the original grains have been incorporated into the planets. The rest were blown out of the solar system when the young Sun exhaled a high velocity 'wind' of gases. Nevertheless, a dilute sprinkling of dust orbits the Sun between the planets. Also, in 1983, Japanese researchers found a denser ring of dust particles orbiting the Sun closer than the planet Mercury. Belts of dust were also found in the asteroid belt between Mars and Jupiter.

Interplanetary dust in our solar system is formed from two sources—the asteroid belt and comets. Asteroids are very small planets (the total mass of all asteroids is less than our Moon) that orbit the Sun between Mars and Jupiter. The asteroids would probably have coalesced to form a major planet but for the gravitational influence of the giant Jupiter. Collisions between asteroids produce cosmic dust.

Many astronomers believe that icy dust grains in the outer part of the early solar system, unaffected by the heat of the infant Sun, coalesced into icy bodies a few tens of kilometres across—cometary nuclei. A storage cloud of cometary material exists far beyond the orbit of Pluto. This is the Oort Cloud. Occasionally the gravitational effect of passing stars may send a comet hurtling inwards towards the Sun. The heat of the Sun evaporates the comet's ices and jets of steam and gas spurt out to form the coma (head) and tail of the comet. These jets dislodge grains from the cometary nucleus.

In 1986 European and Soviet spacecraft flew past Halley's Comet and viewed it close up. The comet was ejecting twelve tonnes of dust per second. Three kinds of dust grains were found; some grains were rocky silicates, the majority were a mixture of silicates and organic molecules and the third type consisted entirely of organic molecules.

A small dust grain entering Earth's atmosphere burns up with frictional energy and is seen as a meteor or shooting star. On the other hand, meteorites are much larger and much of the mass can survive passage through the atmosphere to hit the ground. Meteorites are not really cosmic dust. They are larger splinters of rock or iron, broken off in a collision between two asteroids.

Interstellar dust is made by old dying stars. Nuclear reactions inside a star convert hydrogen and helium into heavier elements, such as oxygen, silicon and carbon. When a star gets old it expands into a red giant and the temperature at the surface drops so low that some of the gases condense into solids. Depending on its history a star may be rich in either carbon or oxygen. A carbon star emits a pall of soot: carbon grains. If the star contains more oxygen than carbon, the oxygen reacts with silicon and other metals to form silicates thereby producing the larger silicate grains which are the major components of interstellar dust.

The Strange Case of Dark Matter

The kind of matter that constitutes our bodies, the general biological world and the Earth on which we live is composed of atoms made from subatomic particles called protons, neutrons and electrons. Matter as we know it contains ninety-two naturally occurring elements, ranging from hydrogen (the lightest) to uranium (the heaviest). No doubt, the majority of people think that the universe is composed entirely of this 'baryonic matter'. However, astronomers estimate that such ordinary matter may constitute as little as one per cent of the matter in the universe. They infer that the remaining matter in the universe is of a different kind and it has been given the name 'dark matter'. The nature of this dark matter has yet to be determined.

This strange type of matter is called dark matter to indicate that it cannot be directly detected (at least it has not been possible to do so to date). It is electrically neutral and does not emit light or other electromagnetic radiation. However, because it is matter, it is attracted to all other matter by the force of gravitational attraction. This property has allowed dark matter to be detected indirectly.

In order to understand how the presence of dark matter in the universe has been indirectly detected, it is helpful to briefly consider two very different forms of the circular rotation of bodies around a central axis. One example is our solar system which consists of a massive central Sun around which nine planets revolve, each in a distinct elliptical orbit. Each planet is held in orbit by its gravitational attraction to the Sun. The planet Mercury orbits closest to the Sun, Venus orbits next closest, and so on out to Pluto which orbits furthest out from the Sun. Mercury rushes around the Sun at a great rate and completes its orbit in three months. In contrast, it takes Pluto two hundred and fifty years to complete one orbit. The reason for the large time difference is not only that Mercury's orbit is much shorter than Pluto's, but that the gravitational power of the Sun exerts a greater pull on Mercury than it does on Pluto, thereby causing Mercury to move faster than Pluto.

Another example of circular rotation is an old fashioned vinyl record rotating on the turntable of the record player. Equivalent points at every radius from the centre of the disc take the same time to complete one orbit. Therefore, the further a point is from the centre of the disc, the greater is its speed of revolution, which is the opposite of the behaviour of the planets in our solar system. In the latter case, motive force is supplied by the gravitational attraction to the central Sun, which gets weaker with distance from the Sun. With the revolving disc, the attractive forces between the molecules in the disc hold them closely together and the disc revolves as a single piece.

Galaxies contain billions of stars. The distribution of the stars in a spiral galaxy is uneven. There is a dense central cluster of stars and the density of star distribution becomes more dilute as you proceed out from the central hub. The three dimensional shape of a spiral galaxy roughly resembles that of a fried egg, with the central yolk representing the dense central hub of stars. Galaxies rotate and astronomers can measure the speed of rotation. Careful observations have shown that, once you move out a relatively short distance from the centre of the galaxy, all of the stars from there to the outer edge of the galaxy rotate at the same speed. When the sums are done to calculate the gravitational forces needed to effect this result, it is clear that the galaxy contains far more matter than is visible. This is the dark matter of the galaxy.

It is estimated that the visible matter in a galaxy constitutes only several per cent of the total matter in the galaxy. There are also clouds of gas and dust between the stars, composed of baryonic matter. It is estimated that the total baryonic matter content of a galaxy is around twenty per cent. Eighty per cent of the mass of the galaxy is composed of dark matter. The proportion of dark matter increases when you consider larger volumes of the universe. Much evidence indicates that clusters of galaxies are at least ninety per cent dark matter.

These relative proportions of baryonic and dark matter have fundamental implications for cosmology (the understanding of the origin, development and the future of the universe). The current cosmological working model is the Big Bang Theory. The details of this theory predict a certain density of baryonic matter in the universe. The oldest stars in the universe, presumably made of the primordial stuff of the universe, are composed of twenty-six per cent helium and seventy-four per cent hydrogen. In order to produce this mixture of gases at the beginning, the details of the Big Bang Theory predict that you cannot have more than a few per cent of the critical amount of matter today in the form of baryons.

What is the nature of this dark matter? The answer to this question is not known, but there is no shortage of suggestions. Physicists have long since overcome any shyness they might have felt at proposing the existence of new particles and have given full rein to their creative imaginations in proposing particles as candidates for dark matter. Some proposed candidates include neutrinos, photinos, higgsinos, gravitinos and axions. Many of the proposed particles have never been seen. However, neutrinos are known to exist and the Big Bang model predicts that the universe contains as many neutrinos as photons. It is unclear yet as to whether or not they possess mass. Some recent experiments have indicated that the neutrino does have a tiny mass—a few millionths of the mass of an electron. The neutrino is probably the current best bet as to the nature of at least some of the dark matter.

Many physicists believe that we are on the verge of proposing a credible Theory of Everything—the ultimate description of the nature of the material world. I am puzzled as to why they think we are so close to a Theory of Everything when we are still so far from understanding the nature of the preponderance of matter in the universe.

Planets Beyond our Solar System

When you look at the night sky through a telescope the only planets you can see are those in our own solar system. Everything else that is visible is a star (sun). Direct evidence for the existence of planets beyond our solar system only became available in the last few years.

I first became aware about ten years ago that no-one had ever seen a planet outside our solar system. I was very surprised. After all, it is commonly assumed that every second sun in the galaxy has a planet, or planets, rotating around it. Many people also think, sometimes passionately, that a lot of these planets harbour life. Giordano Bruno was burnt at the stake in 1600 for teaching that the universe is infinite and full of inhabited planets.

You can see an object through a telescope because it magnifies light from the object. Stars are readily visible because each is a nuclear reactor radiating light energy with intense luminosity. Planets do not radiate light and can be seen only by detecting the light reflected off them from their neighbourhood star. However, from afar, the relatively tiny amount of light reflected by planets is lost in the glare of the intense light emitted by the star. The effect of glare can be easily appreciated by noting that the stars, so clearly visible in our night sky, become invisible in the Sun's daytime glare.

The first planet to be detected outside our solar system was announced in 1995 by two astronomers from the University of Geneva in Switzerland. The astronomers did not see the planet. They inferred its presence from the effect it exerts on the star that it orbits. The technique used is Doppler spectroscopy, a well-known method for measuring the speed of a receding or approaching source of radiation.

A Garda speed-trap recently used Doppler spectroscopy to record me driving at 50 mph in a 40 mph zone. They kindly sent me a note to this effect and charged me £50. The technique works as follows. A radar gun fires radiation at a car and the radiation is reflected from the car back to the gun. Radiation is a wave motion and is characterised by wavelength, the distance from peak to peak.

If the car is stationary, the reflected radiation has the same wavelength as when it left the gun. If the car is approaching the gun the wavelength of the reflected radiation is decreased in proportion to the speed of the oncoming car. If the car is receding from the gun, the wavelength of the reflected radiation is increased in proportion to the speed of the receding car. The radar gun reads the wavelength of the reflected radiation and calculates the speed of the car.

Now, consider the planet orbiting the star beyond our solar system. Because of the law of universal gravitation, the planet exerts a gravitational pull on the star. When the planet passes between the Earth and the star, it pulls the star towards the Earth. When the planet orbits the star to the opposite side it pulls the star away from the Earth. The star emits light at certain wavelengths and these wavelengths can be measured by telescopes on Earth. Because of the pull of the planet on the star these wavelengths are successively shortened and lengthened as they arrive on Earth as the star is successively pulled towards the Earth and then away from the Earth by the planet. Observation of oscillating wavelengths coming from the star convinced the astronomers of the presence of a planet.

The star observed by the Swiss astronomers is about the size and temperature of our Sun and is readily seen in the skies of the northern hemisphere. The planet is large, about the size of Jupiter, and orbits the star at a radius of about five million miles, taking 4.2 days to complete an orbit. By contrast, the innermost planet in our solar system, Mercury, orbits the Sun at a radius of thirty-six million miles and completes one orbit in eighty-eight days.

Other workers were also searching for extra-solar planets using Doppler spectroscopy, but nobody was looking for a planet as big as Jupiter, orbiting close to a star. Workers at San Francisco State University reanalysed their data after the Swiss announcement and uncovered evidence of several new planets. By the end of 1996 astronomers had identified six new planets, all of them orbiting stars similar to our Sun.

Almost all the extra-solar planets so far discovered are at least as big as Jupiter. The explanation for this coincidence is that the Doppler spectroscopic technique is presently not sensitive enough to detect the pulling power of a planet smaller than Jupiter. However, a really puzzling fact is that these large planets orbit their suns much closer than can be explained by conventional understanding of how solar systems are born.

It is believed that a solar system begins as a large cloud of gas and dust. A condensation of gas at the centre of the cloud becomes the central star and the solid cores of the planets in a solar system form from the surrounding disc of gas and dust. The central star begins to burn and the heat drives away the gas that remains close to it. Therefore one expects the innermost planets to be small and rocky, as in our solar system. Only in the outer reaches of the solar system will enough gas (hydrogen and helium) be available to form gassy planets like Jupiter, Saturn, Uranus and Neptune.

Astronomers feel certain that only the densest clouds, from which solar systems form, contain enough rocky material to form rocky planets as big as the Earth. Jupiter is a thousand times the volume of the Earth and rocky planets this size seem to be out of the question. It is assumed therefore that the newly discovered extra-solar planets are gassy giants. Perhaps each was originally formed, as theory would predict, far out from the Sun in its solar system and later something happened causing it to spiral in closer to the star. Or perhaps they are a kind of object new to astronomers.

This is a fast-moving field. The Hubble Space Telescope recently photographed eerie discs of dust around young stars hundreds of light years away. These discs are probably early formative stages of a planetary system.

The Solar System and the Earth

The Planets in our Solar System

Nine planets orbit the Sun. Other orbital components of the solar system include asteroids, comets and rings of interplanetary dust. Until as recently as thirty years ago, astronomers knew relatively little about the planets, with the exception of our own Earth. Much more is now known and acquisition of knowledge has been greatly assisted by the various space probes.

There are nine major planets and they are usually divided into two groups—the inner planets and the outer planets. In moving outwards from the Sun, you meet the planets in the following order: Mercury, Venus, Earth and Mars (the inner planets); Jupiter, Saturn, Uranus, Neptune and Pluto (the outer planets). The inner planets are small and are mainly composed of rocks and iron. With the exception of Pluto, the outer planets are large and mainly composed of hydrogen, helium and ice. So, we can divide the planets into rocky dwarfs and gassy giants.

Mercury, Venus and Mars are similar in density to Earth and must be composed largely of rock, possibly with iron cores. The next four planets, Jupiter, Saturn, Uranus and Neptune, are much larger than Earth and have much lower densities than Earth. Saturn has such a low density it would float in water. The low density means that these planets must be composed mainly of gases and liquids. Tiny Pluto is at the edge of the solar system and is probably composed of a mixture of rock and ice.

Mercury has only a transient atmosphere and its surface is still scarred by the bombardment of asteroids it received early in its history. Carbon dioxide is only a minor constituent of the Earth's atmosphere, but the atmosphere of Venus consists almost entirely of carbon dioxide (ninety-six per cent). This causes such a large greenhouse effect that the surface temperature of Venus is the hottest of all the planets at 477°C.

The only planet with abundant liquid water and life is Earth. We earthlings long entertained notions that Mars harbours life—even intelligent life. At the beginning of the twentieth century, Percival Lowell made detailed observations of the planet and formulated a theory of an advanced civilisation on Mars that had built an elaborate system of canals in order to use scarce water supplies for irrigation purposes.

Lowell also predicted the presence of a planet beyond Neptune, which was discovered in 1930 and named Pluto. Although the concept of a Martian civilisation did not survive Lowell's death in 1916, the idea that biological life exists on Mars was widely accepted for most of the twentieth century. However, this notion was finally disproved by the Viking mission to Mars in 1976. There is no evidence for the existence of life on Mars now, although the planet may have harboured life in the past. And, almost certainly, there is no life anywhere else in our solar planetary system outside our own beautiful Earth.

Although there is evidence that Mars once had liquid water on the surface, the carbon dioxide atmosphere is now so thin that the planet is dry and cold. It has an average temperature of -55°C, with polar caps of solid carbon dioxide (dry ice). About half of Mars is heavily cratered, but the rest is different, with vast volcanoes and canyons larger than anything on Earth. In terms of the age of the solar system there has been recent geological activity on Mars—lava flows and water erosion have erased the older craters.

Among the giant planets (Jupiter, Saturn, Uranus and Neptune), Jupiter and Saturn are supergiants. Together they contain over ninety per cent of the mass of all the planets. Both planets are composed predominantly of hydrogen and helium. Models indicate that both planets have rocky cores. Both planets have intricate ring systems and satellites.

Detailed observations have been made of the rings around Saturn, Neptune and Uranus by the Voyager spacecraft. The rings of Uranus and Neptune are very narrow (a few kilometres thick) and they orbit the planets at a distance of around 50,000 km. The broad rings of Saturn are composed of thousands of narrow 'ringlets', nestling together, one inside the other. The rings are composed of millions of lumps of ice, ranging in size from a few millimetres up to a few metres.

Astronomers have pieced together the story of how the solar system was formed. About four and a half billion years ago, a cloud of gas and dust collapsed under its own gravity to form a clump at the centre, which became our Sun, and a swirling disc of dust and gas (hydrogen and helium), which later formed the planets. The dust consisted of tiny grains of ice and rock. Closer to the Sun the heat evaporated most of the ice particles, leaving the rock grains. This explains why the planets near the Sun are rocky.

Further out from the Sun the icy particles survived and the planets Uranus and Neptune are composed of rock and ice (melted). Saturn and Jupiter began in this way, but became so big that their gravity captured hydrogen and helium from the disc and they now consist principally of these gases.

Planets are thought to have started to form when dust particles clumped together to form 'planetesimals', a few kilometres wide. The planetesimals in turn merged to form the planets. After the nine main planets were formed they quickly swept up most of the remaining planetesimals. The impacts made by the colliding planetesimals are evident in the cratering still visible on all the old surfaces that have survived in the solar system. This old cratering is no longer visible on Earth, having been gradually removed by geological erosion.

There is evidence that our Moon was formed when a body about the size of Mars crashed into the Earth. The collision threw out a spray of molten rock from Earth that condensed into particles which in turn aggregated to form the Moon.

The Importance of the Sun

On 2 December, 1995, NASA launched a US–European observatory to study the Sun. Ireland had a special interest in this mission. The observatory had experimental apparatus on board, designed and built at Maynooth College, to study solar wind. Well might we humans study our own star, to which we owe our very existence.

All civilisations in early phases of development worship the Sun. There is nothing at all surprising about this. Of all the objects in our physical environment, the Sun is outstandingly the most important. We owe everything to the Sun and without its heat and light the Earth would be a frozen barren rock containing no life of any sort. The Sun will not live forever. It is currently half way through its estimated lifespan. When the Sun dies, life will no longer be possible on Earth.

The major planets in our solar system.

	Average distance from sun (million km)	Diameter (km)	Mass (Earth = 1)	Density (Water = 1)	No. of satellites	Magnetic field (Earth = 1)	Time to orbit Sun (yrs)
Mercury	58	4,878	0.06	5.4	0	0.01	0.24
Venus	108	12,103	0.82	5.3	0	0	0.62
Earth	150	12,752	1	5.5	1	1	1
Mars	28	6,794	0.11	3.9	2	<0.01	1.88
Jupiter	778	142,800	317.8	1.3	16	14	11.86
Saturn	1,427	120,660	96.1	0.7	20+	0.67	29.46
Uranus	2,870	51,400	14.5	1.2	15	0.1	84.01
Neptune	4,497	49,400	17.2	1.7	2	?	164.79
Pluto	5,900	2,280	0.002	1.99	1	?	247.7

The Sun is a star, and a fairly ordinary one as stars go. It sits at the centre of our solar system. Nine major planets revolve around the Sun, each in a characteristic elliptical orbit of revolution. The closest planet to the Sun is Mercury and then in order come Venus, Earth, Mars, Jupiter, Saturn, Uranus, Neptune and Pluto. The Earth orbits the Sun at an average distance of ninety-three million miles. The Sun is enormous in volume and mass compared to each of the planets. The total mass of the Sun is 330,000 times that of the Earth and 745 times that of all the planets put together. The diameter of the Sun is 109 times greater than the diameter of the Earth.

The Sun is composed almost entirely of the gases hydrogen (seventy per cent) and helium (thirty per cent), with only a trace of heavier elements. The core of the Sun, extending out to a radius of one quarter of the total radius, is a huge nuclear fusion reactor, where hydrogen atoms are fused together to form helium atoms and enormous amounts of energy are released. The temperature at the centre of the Sun is an incredible 15,000,000° C. The energy of the Sun is radiated out into space, mainly in the form of visible light. When this radiation reaches Earth it effectively forms our sole external source of heat and light.

The solar wind is a 'gas' of electrically charged particles that escapes from the Sun and spirals into the solar system. Sudden changes in the solar wind can affect the Earth's magnetic field, and this can disrupt navigation and communication systems, damage electric power networks and disrupt satellites. The Irish experiment on board the NASA observatory will yield valuable information on the effect of solar wind on communication and power networks.

All life on Earth is dependent on the energy received from the Sun. The Sun warms the Earth to a temperature just right to support life—over most of the globe the temperature is such that water remains in its liquid state and is neither frozen solid nor boiled off into a gas. Secondly, most of the food used to maintain biological life on Earth is ultimately made by harnessing the energy of the sunlight that falls on Earth. Also, the fossil fuel stores on Earth, i.e. coal, oil, natural gas and peat, are all organic compounds that were originally made with the vital assistance of sunlight.

All biological organisms on Earth are grouped into various food chains, where each link feeds on the link below and in turn is eaten by the link above. Man eats animals, animals eat plants. Plants, however, do not build up and sustain themselves by eating simpler forms of life. They are endowed with the remarkable capacity to synthesise their own complex molecules by fusing together two simple compounds, carbon dioxide and water, to form carbohydrate (principally glucose) and oxygen. This process is called photosynthesis and is powered by the energy of sunlight.

Photosynthesis takes place in the green leaves of plants. They are green in colour because they contain a pigment (chlorophyll) which traps the energy of the sunlight. Organisms capable of satisfying all their requirements relying entirely on the simplest nutrients such as CO_2 (carbon dioxide), NH_3 (ammonia) and H_2O (water) are called autotrophs.

The vital first step in almost all food chains on Earth depends on photosynthesis. The glucose produced in photosynthesis is the basic chemical fuel required by most organisms to power their activities. Organisms capable of photosynthesis can make their own glucose from the simple compounds carbon dioxide and water. Most other organisms, including all animals, must have glucose presented to them in a pre-synthesised form. These organisms are called heterotrophs. Note also that photosynthesis releases oxygen to the atmosphere.

Only a small fraction of the total photosynthesis on Earth is carried out by the familiar green plant. It has been estimated that some ninety per cent of all photosynthesis is carried out in the seas by various kinds of micro-organisms, including bacteria and algae. If photosynthesis ceased on Earth, the essential starting point for food chains would stop and in a short while life on Earth would starve to death.

The glucose produced in photosynthesis is used by all organisms in processes called glycolysis and respiration in which energy (in the form of a chemical called ATP) is produced. This energy is used to power all organisms' activities and also to build up the structures of the organisms. In respiration glucose is broken down in the presence of oxygen to yield carbon dioxide and water. This process is the opposite to photosynthesis.

Carbon dioxide is released back into the atmosphere during respiration. Undisturbed, nature ensures that photosynthesis and respiration are balanced globally and this helps to regulate the gaseous composition of the atmosphere, particularly the concentration of carbon dioxide.

The annual flow of energy through the biological world each year is enormous. The total amount of carbon converted from the gaseous state of carbon dioxide into biological solid structure by all the photosynthetic organisms on the face of the Earth each year is about 160×10^9 tons. (10^9 is equal to 10 multiplied by itself eight times.) The amount of energy needed to 'fix' this amount of carbon is about 1×10^{18} calories per year. To put this figure in context, it is estimated that the amount of energy expended each year by all the manmade machines on the face of the Earth is no more than about four per cent of the annual flux of biological energy.

Our Sun is presently about five billion years old. It has an estimated life of ten billion years. When the hydrogen fuel in the Sun's core becomes exhausted the Sun will expand to become a red giant star, whose outer layers will reach the orbit of the Earth or beyond. It will remain a red giant for about half a billion years after which it will contract to a white dwarf star about twice the size of the Earth and slowly cool for several billion years. The Earth will be destroyed as a home for life during the red giant phase of the Sun. Of course, the only way for humankind to survive such a cataclysmic event will be to leave the Earth well in advance and to colonise another planet. We have about five billion years to prepare for this.

The Earth's Reversible Magnetic Field

The Earth behaves like a giant bar magnet whose axis runs north–south. The northern magnetic pole lies in the Arctic, about 1,600 kilometres from the geographical north pole. The southern magnetic pole lies in the Antarctic, about 2,600 kilometres from the southern geographical pole. The direction of the Earth's magnetic field, although relatively steady over long periods of time, completely reverses itself every several hundred thousand years. In other words, what was the northern magnetic pole becomes the southern magnetic pole, and vice versa. Geological evidence now tells us that a reversal in direction of the Earth's magnetic field is long overdue.

Magnetism is an aspect of the electromagnetic force, which is one of the four fundamental forces in nature. These four forces are gravity, electromagnetism, the strong nuclear force and the weak nuclear force. Electric and magnetic forces are intimately connected. Electric charges in motion produce a magnetic force. A moving magnet induces an electric current. A magnetic force field organises itself in space between two opposite poles, north and south. The lines of force radiate outwards from the poles. The origin of magnetic force derives from the behaviour of electrons in atoms. Some elements, such as iron, display strong magnetic properties; other elements do not. An existing magnetic field can induce magnetism in a non-magnetised piece of metal—for example, if you rub a bar magnet against a thin sliver of iron, the sliver will itself become a bar magnet and, if free to move, will line itself up along the Earth's magnetic field, with one end pointing towards the north magnetic pole and the other towards the south magnetic pole. The sliver has become a magnetic compass.

The word 'magnet' comes from magnetite, the Greek term for a strongly magnetic oxide of iron, which occurs naturally in some parts of the world. The Chinese seem to have been the first people to interpret the directional properties of magnets. Around the first century BC they were using finely pivoted magnetised spoons in order to predict the future. It was not until the twelfth century that records show they used compass needles as a navigational aid.

One of the first attempts to explain the unerring tendency of a compass needle to point north–south was the thirteenth century suggestion by Pierre de Maricourt that the behaviour was due to an attractive force exerted by the North Star, which is the only celestial body to remain fixed in the heavens. Most of his contemporaries, however, thought that the behaviour of the compass was dictated by the presence of strong magnetic mountains in the Arctic region. Critics of this view pointed out that magnetic mountains had been seen by travellers all over the world, but no such mountains had been observed in the Arctic Circle.

It is now known that the Earth's magnetic field originates from within the Earth itself. If you could cut a section through the Earth, passing through the centre, and examine the exposed interior you would find that the Earth is built rather like an onion with many layers lying on top of each other. Unlike the onion, the layers are not all of equal thickness. The depth from the surface of the Earth to its centre is approximately 6,370 kilometres. On the outside of the Earth is the thin crust. Beneath the crust, three layers, down to a depth of almost 3,000 kilometres, are collectively referred to as the mantle. The inner two layers of the Earth are called the outer core and the inner core. The outer core is fluid, the inner core is solid. As the Earth rotates on its axis, the outer core fluid layer allows the mantle and solid crust to rotate relatively faster than the solid inner core. As a consequence it is claimed that electrons in the core move relative to those in the mantle and crust. This movement creates a natural dynamo and therefore a magnetic field similar in shape to the field of a bar magnet.

There have been several reports over the centuries, from various parts of the world, of compass needles behaving strangely when placed over certain rocks. It was reported that the north pointing end of the compass needle would swing around to point south and, of course, the previously south pointing end would now point northwards. In 1963, two research groups convinced most geophysicists that such rocks are evidence of a past reversal in the Earth's magnetic field—records of a time when the northern magnetic pole resided where the southern pole is today. These volcanic rocks are

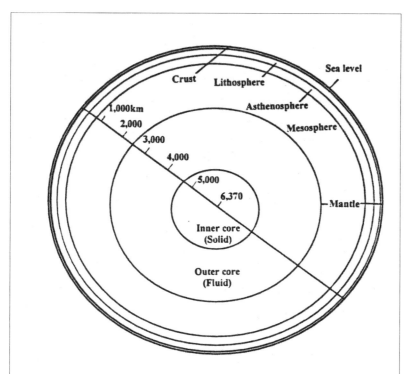

The layers of the Earth. The Earth is not a perfect sphere, but is flattened somewhat at the poles and bulges somewhat at the equator. This effect is exaggerated in the illustration.

'magnetic fossils' recording the intensity and direction of the global magnetic field that prevailed when the rocks cooled and hardened. Rocks from widely scattered parts of the world, but of about the same age, display reverse polarity. The Earth's poles have flipped over up to twenty-five times during the past five million years—on average, once every 200,000 years. The last flip-over happened 730,000 years ago, so we are now long overdue for another magnetic reversal. Geologists explain the reversals as being caused by eddies and currents in the outer core. When these currents predominantly flow in one direction the magnetic north pole is situated where it is today. When they predominantly flow in the opposite direction, the magnetic north pole will flip over to occupy the present position of the magnetic south pole.

The evidence indicates that the flip-over in the polarity of the Earth's magnetic field does not occur all of a sudden but is preceded by a gradual weakening of the field. Some measurements of the present rate of decline of field strength of the Earth's magnetic field suggest that a flip-over will occur in 2,000 years' time. By the time this happens we may be so well forewarned and forearmed that it will cause little disruption to human activities. Of course, if it happened suddenly, the magnetic guidance systems of ships, aeroplanes, spacecraft and missiles would all go awry. When the flip-over does eventually happen it would seem inevitable that bacteria, insects, fish and birds that use the magnetic field to orient themselves will experience trouble finding their bearings. World climate may also change for the worse. As the Earth's magnetic field weakens prior to flipping over, radiation particles from the Sun, that previously remained at the outer edge of the Earth's magnetic field, may pass through the upper atmosphere providing nuclei for the formation of vast banks of ice clouds that could cause cold rainy weather. The weakened magnetic field will also allow more cosmic radiation to reach the surface of the Earth, thereby increasing natural mutation rates in biological organisms.

The Global Earthquake Threat

Recent earthquakes, for example, in Kobe, Japan, on 17 January, 1995, captured media headlines and evoked great sympathy world-wide for the victims and for the surviving members of their families. The Kobe earthquake killed over 6,000 people and caused damage estimated at between ten and twenty trillion Yen (between 70–140 billion Irish punts). Horrific earthquakes may become increasingly more common in the future because of the locations of many of the world's large and fastest growing cities.

The Russian earthquakes of the late 1980s were major disasters. The Armenian earthquake which occurred on 7 December, 1988, had particularly horrendous consequences. It killed 30,000 people, injured as many more and destroyed vast amounts of property. The Tadzhikistan earthquake on 23 January, 1989, killed 1,000 people.

The Armenian earthquake measured 9.6 on the Richter scale. An earthquake of this dimension occurs somewhere in the world about once every month. Normally such earthquakes are of little consequence because they occur in very sparsely populated regions. The Russian earthquakes in the late 1980s were devastating, not because the tremors were unusually severe, but because they occurred in areas of high population. Unfortunately, over one third of the world's largest cities are located in areas that are susceptible to earthquakes.

The science of geology has discovered that the spherical Earth is made up of numerous layers, somewhat like an onion. The layers differ from each other in composition, density and physical consistency. We live on the crust of the Earth which is the surface of the outer solid layer (the lithosphere) of our globe. The lithosphere is only seventy kilometres deep and the crust itself represents only about one per cent of the Earth's volume. Beneath the solid lithosphere is a layer called the asthenosphere which is about two hundred kilometres deep. The rocks of the Earth contain naturally occurring radioactive elements that are continually disintegrating. Heat is released during the radioactive disintegration. This heat cannot be easily dissipated under the high pressure conditions that exist within the Earth. The temperature is high in the asthenosphere, largely because of this radioactive decay. The heat tends to melt the rocks and they may even flow.

The lithosphere of the Earth is therefore sitting on a partially molten underlayer. The lithosphere has a number of faults or cracks running through it and those faults divide it into several great segments called plates. These great plates, bearing the continents and oceans of the world, move slowly relative to each other on the underlying pliable asthenosphere. In some places neighbouring plates bump into each other; in other places they slide past each other and in yet other places, one plate dips beneath the neighbouring plate edge. The movements of the Earth's great plates explain many geological phenomena, including earthquakes and volcanoes. The general theory of plate movement and associated phenomena is known as plate tectonics.

Probably the best known tectonic fault is called the San Andreas Fault that runs along the western edge of California, dividing the American plate from the Pacific plate. The American and Pacific plates slide laterally relative to each other and areas lying along and near the fault are consequently at risk from earthquakes. Famous earthquakes that have occurred in the past associated with this fault and its southern extension are the San Francisco earthquake of 1906 which killed five hundred people and the earthquake that devastated Mexico City in 1985 killing 100,000 people.

A recent survey shows that approximately forty per cent of the world's largest cities are situated either close to a tectonic plate boundary or near where an earthquake has occurred in the past. Each of these cities has more than two million inhabitants. In total, over 600 million people will live in these cities by the year 2035. Since these cities are situated in areas of high seismic risk, the stage may be set for unprecedented major disasters. The figure opposite shows the world's plate boundaries in relation to the major cities.

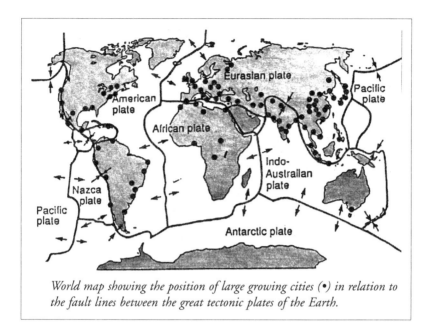

World map showing the position of large growing cities (•) in relation to the fault lines between the great tectonic plates of the Earth.

Most of the deaths that occur in an earthquake are caused by falling buildings. It follows, therefore, that the construction of buildings that are resistant to earthquakes should lessen the loss of life. It is widely acknowledged that much of the damage in the recent Armenian earthquake resulted from the collapse of poorly constructed buildings. In recent years many new multi-storey apartment blocks were built in the region to cope with the growing population. These were often built with low quality concrete, badly designed joists and lacked steel reinforcements. Similarly, many of the new fast growing cities in the world, situated in regions of high seismic risk, contain only basic shelter for people and not earthquake resistant buildings.

While much of the damage from future earthquakes will probably occur in the Third World, cities in the developed world are certainly not earthquake-proof. Tokyo is probably the most earthquake conscious city in the world. It was destroyed by an earthquake in 1923, which killed more than 100,000 people. Elaborate precautions have been incorporated into the present city in order to limit the damage that a future earthquake might cause. In spite of this, a recent study estimates that an earthquake measuring 9.5 on the Richter scale occurring just east of Japan (similar to the 1923 earthquake) would destroy about 2,500,000 buildings, cause about 150,000 deaths and 200,000 injuries.

What is the risk that Ireland would ever suffer a significant earthquake? Ireland is a very stable land with little risk of a major earthquake. The early annals record earthquakes felt in Ireland, but most did little or no damage. An exception occurred in Co. Sligo in 1490 when it is recorded that one hundred people were killed along with many horses and cows, and a lake opened up.

Most earthquakes felt in Ireland are minor and many of them originate in Britain or in the Irish Sea. There is a zone along the Irish coast from Cork to Dublin that is active and produces small earthquakes from time to time. The most active area is near Enniscorthy in Co. Wexford. In 1985 this centre produced an earthquake of magnitude 2 on the Richter scale. Activity was also reported in September 1988.

Irish earthquakes are minor events caused by the relaxation of stressed rocks. They are not connected with plate movement. The nearest plate boundary to Ireland is the Mid-Atlantic Ridge which is about 2,500 km to the west. This is an active area and it is not impossible, although highly unlikely, that a major earthquake on the ridge could cause damage in Ireland. In 1755 such an earthquake destroyed Lisbon, killing 60,000 people. The damage was completed by a tidal wave. These waves are produced at the sea bottom by the earthquake shock. They have great energy and wreak havoc when they reach land. Perhaps ancient tales of huge unexpected waves hitting the Irish coast record tidal waves produced by earthquakes in the Mid-Atlantic.

Some Laws of Physics

The Laws of Thermodynamics

Energy is the capacity to do work. Thermodynamics is that branch of physics that deals with energy transformations from one form into another. The three laws of thermodynamics are perhaps the most basic in all science. They call attention to two properties that are fundamentally responsible for the behaviour of matter—energy and entropy. They tell us that the eventual course of all physical events can be summarised by two statements—'the energy of the universe is conserved' and 'the entropy of the universe increases'.

The First Law of Thermodynamics is the easiest to understand. It was formulated in the 1840s by the German physicist Hermann von Helmholtz. It states that energy can neither be created nor destroyed (the law of conservation of energy). The total energy in the universe is constant. We all know that different forms of energy can be converted one into the other, for example mechanical work can be converted into heat by briskly rubbing your hands together. The First Law says that in any of these conversions energy neither increases not decreases—it just changes form. It will never be possible, therefore, to invent a machine that creates more energy than it consumes.

The First Law says nothing about the direction that processes take—this is the province of the Second Law of Thermodynamics, originally conceived in 1850 by the German physicist Rudolf Clausius. He noted that, in any energy conversion, such as the conversion of electric energy into light, some of the energy is wasted—it is converted into heat that is dissipated into the environment. (It will thus never be possible to invent a perpetual motion machine.) That portion of the energy that is unavoidably lost as non-useful heat (unavailable to do work) is called entropy. Entropy is a measure of disorder. The Second Law of Thermodynamics states that the entropy of the universe is continually increasing, since in every process involving a flow of energy there is always some loss.

Clausius reached his conclusions largely by studying heat flow. This included the familiar observation that when two bodies, each at different temperatures, come into contact, heat always flows from the hotter to the cooler body and stops flowing when the temperatures of both bodies reach the same value. There is nothing in the First Law to preclude heat flowing from the cooler to the hotter body, but this never happens spontaneously. Energy would be conserved regardless of the direction of flow. The Second Law predicts the direction in which all spontaneous changes proceed.

In 1872, the Austrian physicist Ludwig Boltzmann first explained the spontaneous flow of heat in terms of an increase in atomic disorder. Boltzmann defined temperature as a measure of the speed of molecules. Molecules in a hot body move quickly, molecules in a colder body move more slowly.

When a hotter block is placed on top of a colder block, the initial state is one of relative order, with faster moving molecules segregated from the slower ones. However, at the interface between the blocks, hotter faster molecules bump into cooler slower ones, sharing energy with them. Gradually over time, higher and lower velocity molecules become completely mixed together top and bottom. Disorder (entropy) has increased overall.

The Second Law says that this process will never spontaneously reverse itself, with all the faster moving molecules again segregating themselves into one block, leaving the slower molecules in the other block. But the Second Law allows this to happen if work is performed on the system from the outside. Entropy can be caused to decrease locally by doing work but, in the process, the entropy of the surroundings beyond the local is increased by a greater amount than the local entropy is decreased and, overall, the entropy of the universe increases.

This concept can be understood by considering the domestic refrigerator. Electrical energy powers the extraction of heat from the inside compartment, which lowers the entropy inside the fridge. The extracted heat is dumped into the room increasing its entropy. The increased room entropy exceeds the localised decreased fridge entropy.

Life is highly organised and therefore low in entropy. Nature gathers various elements from the environment and assembles them into complex living systems, thereby decreasing entropy. This does not violate the Second Law because the assembly of life depends on the expenditure of much work, powered by harnessing the energy of the Sun. While entropy is decreased temporarily on a local level by maintaining life, when the overall sums are done, the entropy of the universe increases. The high grade energy of the stars may be used to temporarily decrease entropy in localised regions of the universe, but there is a constant and inevitable leakage of this energy into entropy. The long-term fate of the universe is a state of total disorder, variously called 'entropic doom' or 'the heat death of the universe'. Some people think the universe always existed. However, the incessant tendency for entropy to increase argues against this. If the universe always existed we would now have entropic doom.

Since temperature represents the speed of molecules we can conceive of absolute zero temperature when molecules are motionless. It can be calculated that absolute zero temperature is reached at $-273.15°$ Celsius. The Third Law of Thermodynamics states that the entropy of a perfect crystal is zero at absolute zero temperature.

The laws of thermodynamics prevail with inexorable sway in the life of the universe and in our individual lives. And yet, most people know nothing of them. The novelist and physicist C. P. Snow (1905–1980) was struck by this and made the observation that knowledge of the Second Law of Thermodynamics should have a recognised cultural value equal to familiarity with a work by Shakespeare.

Absolute Zero Temperature and the Third Law of Thermodynamics

In the last chapter I wrote about the laws of thermodynamics, but I concentrated almost entirely on the First and Second Laws and merely mentioned the Third Law. The Third Law is the subject of this chapter. The Third Law concerns itself with the realm of the very cold and the concept of absolute zero temperature. The Third Law is not treated with the same respect as the First and Second Laws, and sometimes attempts are made to prove it wrong.

Let me first of all briefly state the First and Second Laws of Thermodynamics again. The First Law, the law of conservation of energy, states that energy can neither be created nor destroyed. Don't trust anyone who tries to sell you a machine that generates more energy than it consumes. The Second Law states that when any physical or chemical process occurs, the entropy (disorder) of the universe increases—this is because during every transformation of energy, a certain amount is dissipated and becomes unavailable for doing work. Beware of anyone who tries to sell you a perpetual motion machine.

Heat is the most familiar form of energy and temperature is a measure of the degree of heat in a body. As you remove heat from a body, its temperature decreases. If you could remove all the heat, you would have a temperature of absolute zero. The two most familiar temperature scales are the Celsius scale and the Fahrenheit scale. Water freezes at 0° Celsius and boils at 100° Celsius. The two corresponding Fahrenheit temperatures are 32° and 212° Fahrenheit.

It is a relatively straightforward matter to calculate a theoretical value of absolute zero temperature. Take a fixed quantity of a gas and measure its volume at 100° Celsius. Now remove heat and measure the volume of the gas at temperatures of 75°, 50°, 25°, 0°, −25° Celsius, and so on down. Eventually the gas will liquefy (at about −196° Celsius in the case of nitrogen). Now plot a graph of volume versus temperature and extrapolate the line down to zero volume. The corresponding temperature is −273.15° Celsius. This must be the lowest possible temperature, since it cannot be possible to go to a negative volume. The absolute scale of temperature, also called the Kelvin scale, starts at zero for absolute zero and goes upwards in absolute degree units, each equal in size to one unit on the Celsius scale. The freezing and boiling points of water on the Kelvin scale are therefore 273.15° and 373.15° Kelvin respectively.

The Austrian physicist Ludwig Boltzmann defined temperature as a measure of the speed of molecules in a substance. In a hot gas, the molecules are moving about at great speed. When the gas is cooled, the molecules move about more slowly. At absolute zero, pictured in this way, molecules and atoms come to rest. Boltzmann proved that the total amount of disorder increases when heat flows from a hot to a cold body. Also, of course, in a single body, disorder generally increases as temperature rises and decreases as temperature drops. And this is where the Third Law of Thermodynamics comes in. It was proposed in 1906 by Walther Nernst (1864–1941) of the University of Berlin, for which he won the 1920 Nobel prize in Chemistry. The quantum mechanical description of matter emerging at that time says that atoms can never come to complete rest. Even in their lowest energy state (ground state) they still 'vibrate'. This ground state energy cannot be shared with other atoms and doesn't count as heat or disorderliness.

Nernst defined absolute zero temperature in terms of absence of disorder, rather than in terms of absence of motion. The Third Law states that the entropy, or disorder, of a perfect crystal is zero at absolute zero temperature. Some years later when studying the amount of heat lost per unit of temperature decrease approaching absolute zero, he noted that each step was more difficult than the preceding one. He concluded that an infinite amount of effort would be required to reach absolute zero and added a rider to the Third Law to the effect that a temperature of absolute zero can never be attained experimentally.

A similar barrier to the one that prevents the experimental attainment of absolute zero is the one that precludes the acceleration of any material body to the speed of light. When a body accelerates, its mass increases by a small amount, but this increase becomes very significant at speeds approaching the speed of light. As the mass increases rapidly, it becomes progressively more difficult to further accelerate. An infinite amount of effort would thus be required to accelerate to the speed of light, which is therefore precluded.

It is not difficult to appreciate in a qualitative way why it would be impossible to reach absolute zero temperature in an ordinary lump of matter. Such a lump will contain many trillions of molecules at least and, in accordance with the definition of temperature, at absolute zero temperature each and every molecule must be in its ground state. Even if a few molecules start to jiggle about the temperature will rise above absolute zero. It would seem to be a statistical impossibility to dragoon each and every one of such an enormous number of molecules into absolute immobility.

On the other hand, a single atom could readily fall into its ground state. Does this therefore mean that, in this instance, the achievement of absolute zero temperature is experimentally possible? Well no, because temperature is a statistical property and depends by definition on numbers of molecules that can interact with each other. But somewhere between the single molecule and the large lump of matter is a grey area which has just enough molecules to make the concept of temperature feasible, but is still very small—objects of this size are said to be mesoscopic. Some scientists feel that it just might be possible to experimentally persuade this number of atoms to sit quietly and therefore to achieve the Holy Grail of cryogenics (low temperature science)—a temperature of absolute zero. Elaborate experiments are in place at several centres in order to try to achieve this. I believe that the record for the lowest temperature achieved to date stands at 280 picokelvins, i.e. 280 millionths of a millionth of one degree above absolute zero temperature.

I would be surprised if absolute zero temperature could ever be attained. In order to record the event, a thermometer will have to adjudicate. I cannot imagine how it will ever be possible to intervene sufficiently to measure the temperature without adding a tiny bit of heat and thereby inevitably 'spooking' the quarry into a last-minute getaway.

Einstein's Special Theory of Relativity

Albert Einstein published his Special Theory of Relativity in 1905. This was a radical advance on the concepts of classical physics. The Special Theory describes how the world looks to an observer moving at constant speed. It contradicts our 'common-sense' notions. Because the speed of light is constant for all such observers, moving rulers shrink, moving masses grow in mass and moving clocks run slow. In this chapter I will try to briefly explain the main features of Einstein's Special Theory of Relativity.

Prior to Einstein, science accepted that observers moving at a steady velocity relative to each other each find the laws of mechanics to be the same. However, mechanical experiments are affected by movements of the Earth so that experimental results never perfectly match theory. The laws of mechanics work perfectly only in a frame of reference that is at absolute rest. But what part of the universe is at absolute rest? This greatly puzzled physicists. It was postulated that absolute rest is represented by the ether, a ghostly substance that permeates the entire universe, and to which matter is as porous as a sponge is to water.

The ether also conveniently explained the movement of light through a vacuum. James Clerk Maxwell had shown that light is an electrical-magnetic wave that travels through a vacuum at a speed (C) of 186,000 miles per second. But if light is a wave, something must be waving—presumably the ether. According to Maxwell's equations, light moves at only one velocity— C. Maxwell assumed that this velocity was relative to the stationary ether.

In 1887, Albert Michelson and Edward Morley performed an experiment to measure the motion of the Earth through the ether. A beam of light was split into two parts, one part aimed along the direction of the Earth's path through space and the other part aimed at right angles to this direction. It was reasoned that the light aimed along the Earth's path would be heading straight into the 'ether wind' and would be slowed relative to the speed of the light moving across the wind. (Every sailor knows that you travel faster across the wind than into the wind.) Surprisingly, the experiment showed that light moved at the same speed regardless of its direction of movement. In other words, there was no evidence for the existence of the ether.

Measurements of the speed of light always gave the same answer, regardless of the motion of the observer. This finding was puzzling and contradicted the common-sense of classical physics. For example, if you stand opposite a friend, say at a hundred yards distance, and he throws a ball towards you at a speed of ten miles per hour, you will observe the ball moving, relative to you, at ten miles per hour. On the other hand, if you run towards your friend at a speed of ten miles per hour, and he again propels the ball towards you with the same energy as before, you now observe the ball moving at twenty miles per hour relative to yourself. However, if you repeat this experiment and substitute a source of light for the ball, you will always measure the velocity of light at 186,000 miles per second!

Einstein looked afresh at the situation and decided that the ether didn't exist. He transformed the *puzzle* of the constant speed of light into the *principle* of the constant speed of light. In abolishing the ether, Einstein also abolished the primacy of the idea of absolute non-motion. He declared that all the laws of nature are identical in all frames of reference that move uniformly relative to each other and, therefore, there is no way to distinguish

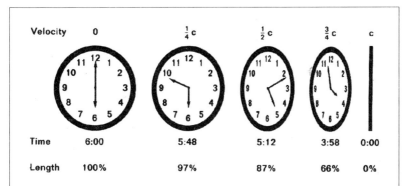

If a set of five clocks in relative motion are synchronised at twelve o' clock, six hours later (by the clock at rest relative to us) they will read differently and have different linear dimensions, depending on their relative velocities. C is the speed of light.

absolutely uniform motion from non-motion. In a railway carriage, from which you cannot see out, moving perfectly smoothly at steady speed in a straight line, there is no experiment you can perform which will tell you whether the carriage is moving or is stationary. The other cornerstone of the Special Theory of Relativity is that the velocity of light is the same in all frames of reference moving uniformly relative to each other.

How do we explain the constant speed of light regardless of the motion of the observer? In order to measure speed, one must use a ruler and a clock. Einstein reasoned that these measuring instruments change, depending on their motion, in such a way that the speed of light always appears the same. The changes in the moving ruler and clock are apparent to an observer at relative rest, but not to an observer travelling along with them. Therefore both observers measure the same speed of light and neither detects anything unusual in the measurement or in the apparatus.

Einstein introduced the labels 'proper' and 'relative'. If we are 'stationary' and observe our stationary rods and clocks, we see their *proper* lengths and time. If we observe a rod and clock travelling very fast relative to us, we see their *relative* length and time. Relative length is always shorter than the proper length and relative time is always slower than the proper time. A moving object is observed to contract in its direction of motion as its velocity increases, until it disappears altogether at the speed of light. A moving clock ticks more slowly than a clock at rest (time dilation) and this trend continues until, at the speed of light, it stops altogether.

This time dilation effect is the basis for the well-known twins paradox. In this scenario, an astronaut twin leaves Earth and spends a year of Earth time travelling through space at high speed. Because time passes more slowly for him than for his earthbound brother, he finds when he returns to Earth that he is younger than his twin. This is not science fiction and has been confirmed experimentally. For example, in 1972 four atomic clocks were flown around the world by aircraft. At the end of the trip they were found to be slightly behind the earthbound twin clocks with which they were synchronised before the flight. Time dilation has also been verified by observations on high energy particles, e.g. cosmic rays.

The speed of light is the fastest speed allowed in the universe. The carriers of light energy are called photons. They can travel at the speed of light because they have no mass. But no material body can ever be accelerated to the speed of light because this would require an infinite amount of energy. This is because mass is measured to increase with speed, rising to infinite mass at the speed of light. This effect has often been verified experimentally by noting the increased mass of an electron moving at high velocities.

The length contraction, increasing mass and time dilation consequences of moving at speed become really significant only at velocities close to the speed of light. Measurements made by the methods of classical physics are fine for the speeds of our everyday world. However, measurements made of events moving close to the speed of light can only be made accurately by taking Einstein's theory into account. For example, for Concorde travelling at Mach 2, the length contraction is only two parts in a trillion—less than the width of an atom. However, if Concorde travelled at half the speed of light it would be seen to contract fifteen per cent and its mass would increase correspondingly. In other words, as you approach the speed of light, energy added to make an object move yet faster is largely converted into an increase in mass of the object. There is an equivalence between energy and mass. Einstein expressed this relationship in his famous formula, $E=MC^2$. This equation has been verified experimentally on countless occasions, not the least of which was the explosion of the first atomic weapon.

Classical physics considered time and space to be separate—space is continuous but time moves in a two dimensional line from the past to the present to the future. However, arising from the Special Theory of Relativity, time and space were seen to form a four dimensional (three space dimensions and a dimension of time) space–time continuum. There are no breaks in a continuum. In the traditional picture, events develop with the passage of time. The space–time continuum is more of a static picture where events do not develop—they just are. If we could view the world of the space–time continuum, we would see events that now seem to develop before us as time passes, already existing in total, etched on the fabric of space–time.

The space–time interval between two events is an absolute, but it can appear different to observers in different states of motion. For example, imagine two observers, A and B. A is sitting in the centre of a steadily moving train carriage and B is standing on the platform as the train passes. A light bulb is switched on in the centre of the carriage as the train passes B.

Observer A sees the light hit both end walls of the carriage simultaneously, but B sees the light hit the rear wall of the carriage before it hits the front wall, because the rear wall is moving forward to meet the light. In other words, A and B disagree on the timing of these two events. However, if A and B each feeds their own time and distance measurements into the formula for calculating space–time interval they will both get the same result.

The Special Theory of Relativity is called special because it applies only to frames of reference that move uniformly with respect to each other. Einstein later developed a theory that is valid for frames of reference that move with non-uniform motion (acceleration and deceleration) relative to each other, as well as those moving uniformly. This is the General Theory of Relativity, published in 1915. I will describe this theory in the next chapter.

Einstein's General Theory of Relativity

Einstein's Special Theory of Relativity, published in 1905, describes how the world looks to observers moving in straight lines at steady velocities. Einstein's General Theory of Relativity, published in 1915, describes how the world looks to observers moving in a non-uniform manner, accelerating and decelerating. This theory developed an entirely new understanding of gravity. This new approach was based on the Principle of Equivalence. Einstein's Special and General Theories of Relativity are cornerstones of modern physics and have passed all tests of their validity.

Einstein's insight into the nature of gravity was greatly assisted by his visualisation of standing in a freely falling lift. The lift accelerates towards Earth under gravity at thirty-two feet per second per second, but the man in the lift is weightless, able to push himself from floor to ceiling with ease. Einstein concluded that, since the downwards acceleration exactly cancels out gravity, acceleration and gravity are equivalent to each other—the Principle of Equivalence.

By the same token, a man in a rocket accelerating uniformly through space at thirty-two feet per second per second will feel a force holding him to the floor of the rocket exactly equivalent to the force of gravity. If the man is unable to look out of the rocket, there is no experiment he can perform which will tell him whether the rocket is moving through space or standing stationary on the Earth.

In another 'thought experiment' on the accelerating rocket, Einstein imagined shining a beam of light through a small hole in one wall, aimed across the rocket towards the other wall. If the rocket were moving at constant speed the light would hit the opposite wall at the same height from the floor as the hole on the other wall. But because the rocket is accelerating, the second wall moves up slightly as the light crosses the rocket, and the light hits the second wall at a point slightly lower than the height of the hole on the first wall. In other words, the beam of light seems to bend as it crosses the rocket. According to the Principle of Equivalence, if a beam of light is bent in an accelerated frame of reference, then it will also be bent by the same amount by gravity.

But how can gravity bend a beam of light, since there is no matter in the beam? This is where the concept of the space–time continuum comes in, which I described in my chapter on the Theory of Special Relativity (see page 42). Classical physics viewed space as a continuous phase with three dimensions, and time as a separate two dimensional line that moves inexorably from the past, to the present, and then into the future. But the Special Theory of Relativity showed that space and time are not separate entities. They are bound together into a four dimensional space–time continuum (three space dimensions and one time dimension). All movement takes place in this continuum. The shape of the space–time continuum is bent and distorted by the presence of matter and, according to Einstein, it is these deformations that account for the 'force' of gravity, bend beams of light and cause moving objects to veer off from straight line trajectories. A rule of thumb says: 'Matter tells space how to curve, space tells matter how to move'.

A helpful analogy is to imagine the empty space–time continuum as a flat, stretched rubbery surface. Now place a heavy cannon ball onto this surface. It will produce a marked local depression where it lies. This is how Einstein visualised that a large lump of matter would distort the space–time continuum.

Now imagine a ball-bearing rolling along the elastic surface. It will roll smoothly along in a straight line making only a small indentation. However, if it comes near the cannon ball, the ball-bearing will follow a curved path along the distortion in the elastic surface. This is the modern model for the force of gravity. Objects follow a path of least resistance through space–time, and the path is curved when space–time is distorted. When a ball-bearing, a planet or a beam of light moves near a large mass, it follows a curved path.

The classical concept of gravity describes it as a force of mutual attraction possessed by all bodies of matter. The Law of Gravitation, formulated by Isaac Newton in 1684, states that the gravitational attraction (F) between two bodies is proportional to the product of the masses (M1, M2) of the two bodies, and inversely proportional to the square of the distance (D) between them ($F=GM1M2/D^2$), where G is the gravitational constant.

According to Einstein, Newton's Law of Gravitation is unnecessary. Einstein attributes the 'force' of gravity to acceleration. A stationary object on the Earth is attracted to the centre of the Earth—gravity. How is this attributable to acceleration? Well, whereas in three dimensional space, the object is stationary, in four dimensional space–time the object is in motion along the curvature of the space–time continuum in the neighbourhood of the Earth. Newton's hypothesis is replaced by the hypothesis that the continuum is curved in the neighbourhood of massive objects.

The Theory of General Relativity has passed every test that has been applied to it. For example, it explained the curious way that Mercury orbits the Sun. Mercury is the closest planet to our massive Sun and therefore occupies a space–time that is strongly distorted. Mercury's orbit cannot be completely explained by Newton's theory of gravity. The curious orbit was, however, explained exactly by general relativity. When gravity is weak, the Theory of General Relativity and Newton's inverse square law give the same results. However, in a very strong gravitational field the inverse square law does not apply precisely, whereas general relativity does.

General relativity has satisfactorily explained the strange properties of newly discovered exotic objects such as black holes, pulsars and quasars. Everyone has heard of black holes—bodies that are so intensely dense that not even light can escape their gravitational power. In terms of the concepts of general relativity, a black hole would so distort space–time as to wrap it around itself completely, pinching itself off from the rest of the universe and disappearing from all outside view.

At the end of its life, when its core nuclear fuel is used up, a star eventually collapses under its own gravity. Some collapse to the extent of becoming neutron stars. These can contain as much matter as our Sun, but squeezed into a volume no bigger than a mountain on Earth.

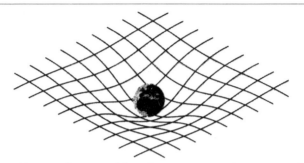

The rubber-membrane model to illustrate gravity: the presence of mass distorts the flat Euclidean space–time continuum.

They have a density approximately the same as the nucleus of an atom, which is close to the density at which a black hole forms. If a neutron star could gain enough extra mass, for example by attracting gas from a neighbouring star, it could succeed in becoming a black hole. A black hole rotating around another star in a binary system would emit X-rays as super-heated gas, stripped from the star, plunges towards the black hole. X-ray sources have been discovered in binary systems with properties matching those predicted for black holes by the general relativity equations.

The Theory of General Relativity also predicts the phenomenon of gravitational radiation. This depends on the concept of space–time as a physical phenomenon which can be distorted by matter. Using the analogy of the elastic sheet for space–time, one can visualise gravity waves arising from the vibrations sent out through the sheet when a lump of matter vibrates. Gravitational radiation is very weak—10^{-40} times the strength of electromagnetic radiation. Elaborate experiments are in progress in order to detect gravitational radiation.

The Theory of Evolution and the Theories of Relativity (Special and General) were the greatest turning points in the history of modern science. The theories, particularly evolution, often attract attempts to prove their invalidity. Attacks on evolution are frequently motivated by religious beliefs. Attacks on relativity are usually argued from a scientific viewpoint. Relativity theory has withstood all tests applied to it and remains a masterpiece and a cornerstone of modern physics.

The Most Famous Equation in the World

I was walking through my local shopping centre recently when a young boy ran past me wearing a T-shirt bearing the legend $E = MC^2$. This famous equation, formulated by Albert Einstein in the year 1907, is the only scientific equation to be popularly familiar. Just as the opening bars of his Fifth Symphony mean Beethoven to a great many people, so the equation $E = MC^2$ means physics and Einstein in the popular consciousness. However, although the equation is widely known, few people understand what it means.

In the equation, E stands for energy, which can be thought of in simple terms as that which makes things move. The unit of energy is called the Joule. M stands for mass (amount of matter), which can be thought of qualitatively as inertia, or resistance to movement. The unit of mass is the kilogram (kg). C stands for the speed of light, which is the maximum velocity allowed in the universe—300,000 km per second (186,000 miles per second). The overall equation says something that is very surprising—that it is possible to turn matter into energy and vice versa.

Because the square of C is such a huge number, the equation tells us that matter is equivalent to incredibly large amounts of energy. For example, to calculate the energy equivalent of a kilogram of sugar (or of anything else) you simply multiply one kilogram by C^2. The resulting figure represents an amount of energy approximately double the total energy usage of the United States of America in one year. Another illustration of the massive amount of energy locked up in matter is the calculation that the complete conversion of one gram of matter into energy would yield as much as the burning of two thousand tons of gasoline.

The first large-scale application to come out of Einstein's famous equation was an unfortunate one—the atomic bomb. The original atomic bomb was based on a process called nuclear fission. Nuclear fission simply means the break-up (fission) of a heavy atom (either uranium or plutonium) into two daughter atoms, each approximately half the size of the parent atom. When you carefully add up the masses of the fission products, you find that the total is slightly less than the mass of the parent atom. The 'lost' mass has been converted into energy. If you take a concentrated lump of uranium or plutonium, you can generate an uncontrolled fission process in which all of the atoms break down in quick succession and a gigantic amount of energy is released—a nuclear explosion. This was the basis for the atomic bombs that were dropped on the cities of Hiroshima and Nagasaki in 1945.

A much more useful application of Einstein's equation was developed after the Second World War. This was to harness the energy contained in matter to generate useful electrical energy. This process is called nuclear power. Nuclear power is also based on the process of nuclear fission. However, in nuclear power, the nuclear fission is managed so that it occurs in a controlled fashion, releasing amounts of energy that can be handled safely and never running away in the uncontrolled manner of an atomic explosion.

The birth of civil nuclear power in the 1950s was heralded with a great fanfare as the dawn of a new age that would satisfy society's energy requirements for the foreseeable future. Unfortunately, nuclear power has been persistently dogged by safety problem and by problems associated with the nuclear waste that it generates. Incidentally, the first civil nuclear power station in the world was the Calder Hall Nuclear Reactor located on the UK Sellafield site. This reactor began operations in 1956 and is still operating today.

The fact that energy and matter are interconvertible is not something we would predict from our everyday intuition. Nevertheless, of the two directions described by the equation, it is easier to get one's head around the conversion of matter into energy than it is to feel comfortable with the idea of the conversion of energy into matter. If we look at the equation $E = MC^2$ again, and rearrange it slightly, we see that $M = E/C^2$. Since C^2 is such a large quantity, and is the divisor in the equation, this tells us that in order to get even the tiniest bit of matter (M), we must convert gigantic amounts of energy (E). We are told that this is what happened at the birth of the universe, when the energy released in the Big Bang explosion radiated out in all directions and then 'froze out' into the matter of the universe. Today, I am unaware of any large-scale practical applications of the principle that energy can be converted directly into matter.

Albert Einstein was born in 1879 in Germany. He lived with his parents in Munich and then in Italy. He taught at the Polytechnic School in Zurich, became a Swiss citizen and was appointed an Inspector of Patents in Berne. During his spare time in the Patent Office, Einstein developed his Special Theory of Relativity, which he presented in 1905. The equation $E = MC^2$ flows from this theory. In 1909 he became a Professor of Theoretical Physics at the University of Zurich. In 1913 he took up a special post of Director of the Kaizer Wilhelm Institute for Physics in Berlin. In 1915 Einstein published his General Theory of Relativity.

Einstein received the Nobel Prize for Physics in 1921 for his explanation of the photoelectric effect (not for his Theory of Relativity). He emigrated to the USA in 1933 after being deprived of his position in Berlin by the Nazis. He spent the remainder of his life in the USA and died in 1955. In addition to his scientific work he also helped many humanitarian causes. In a memorable statement, Einstein declared: 'If my theory of relativity is proven correct, Germany will claim me as a German and France will say I am a citizen of the world. Should my theory prove untrue, France will say that I am a German and Germany will declare that I am a Jew.'

Einstein is the archetypal scientific genius of the twentieth century. Just as one can buy T-shirts bearing his famous equation, one can also buy large poster photographs showing Einstein in his later years. A conspicuous white halo of hair frames a wonderfully lined face. Many books have been written describing Einstein's scientific work and new books continue to emerge every year. Two well-written books on Einstein's work are: *Was Einstein Right?* by C. Will (Basic Books, 1986) and *Subtle is the Lord* by A. Pais (Oxford University Press, 1982).

The Nature of the Very Small: Wave or Particle?

Understanding the nature of the very small is extremely difficult. Few things in the world are more familiar or basic than light. It seems surprising, therefore, that physicists are still struggling to understand the fundamental nature of such a familiar phenomenon.

Isaac Newton (1642–1727) visualised the basic nature of light as a stream of particles. Christian Huygens (1629–1695) developed a wave theory of light, but the significance of his work was dimmed by the shadow of Newton's enormous reputation. The wave theory eventually moved to centre stage when the brilliant experiments of Thomas Young (1773–1829) unambiguously demonstrated the wave-like properties of light.

In Young's experiment light is directed at a board that contains two small slits. A screen on the far side of the board displays the light that traverses the slits. The light forms a pattern of alternating dark and bright stripes on the screen. This pattern, called an interference pattern, can only be explained by treating light as a wave motion.

Light moves from the light source as a circular wave front (just as waves move outwards in a circle when a pebble is dropped in water). When the light hits the board it can only pass through the two slits, each of which now transmits a circular wave front of light beyond the board. Those two spreading wave fronts overlap and interfere with each other before reaching the screen. The bright stripes on the screen represent places where wave crests from one slit meet wave crests from the other and reinforce each other. The dark stripes represent places where wave crests from one slit meet wave troughs from the other and cancel each other out. By measuring the spacing between the dark and the bright stripes, one can calculate the wavelength of the light.

For almost two hundred years, Young's experiment was cited as proof

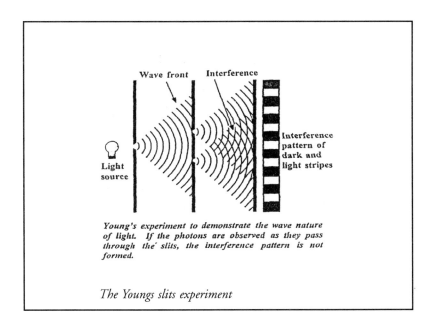

Wave front　　Interference

Light
source

Interference
pattern of
dark and
light stripes

Young's experiment to demonstrate the wave nature of light. If the photons are observed as they pass through the slits, the interference pattern is not formed.

The Youngs slits experiment

that light is a wave. Then, in 1905, Albert Einstein proposed that it was sometimes useful to consider that light acts as a stream of particles (called photons or quanta). The electron, a subatomic particle, was discovered in 1897 by J. J. Thompson. Not only is it unambiguously a particle, but it also carries a negative electric charge. In 1925, Louis de Broglie published a complementary version of Einstein's proposal, claiming that very small bodies, like electrons, can also behave as waves.

In 1925, quantum mechanics—the physics that describes the behaviour of the very small (atoms, subatomic particles, photons)—was invented. It formally proposed that all atomic and subatomic objects have a dual wave/particle nature. Quantum mechanics describes the behaviour of the subatomic world very accurately. However, it has proved extremely difficult to understand the basic nature and concrete reality of things, as opposed to accurately describing and predicting their behaviour.

Young's experiment can also be carried out using electrons and identical results are obtained to those described using ordinary light. This result is completely counter-intuitive. Electrons are definitely particulate—how can they also behave as waves? If you knocked two holes in a wall and threw thousands of balls at the wall you would end up with two distinct piles of balls on the other side, not a series of lines of balls.

The electrons must travel as waves in Young's experiment in order to produce the interference pattern, but they leave the electron source as particles and arrive at the screen as particles (you can see the individual particles showing up as dots as they arrive at the phosphorescent screen). OK, you may say, put a lot of electrons together and they somehow push and jostle each other into a wave pattern. But, amazingly, if you fired the particles through the experiment *one at a time* you would still get the same interference pattern of alternating dark and light stripes. (This last experiment has been carried out using neutrons, but not yet, I think, using electrons.)

Things can get stranger still. If you observe the electrons on their flight through the experiment they react in a very odd manner—the interference pattern disappears and you get a distribution of light on the screen equivalent to the distribution of balls thrown at a wall containing two holes. Even stranger, the same thing happens even if you don't watch the electrons, but if you introduce the *potential* for watching them.

Electrons have a magnetic flag associated with them. Place a device at the left slit that flips the magnetic flags of all the electrons passing through to the up direction and place a device at the right slit that flips the magnetic flags of all the electrons passing through to the down position. You now have the potential to identify the slit through which every electron that arrives at the screen passed on its journey. This in itself makes the interference pattern disappear, whether or not you avail of the potential to identify the slits.

Now go one step further. Interpose a device between the slits and the screen to remove the magnetic flags that would identify the slits. The interference pattern reappears. If you incompletely erase the flag information the sharpness of the interference pattern is degraded to an extent proportional to the extent of removal of the tagging.

It seems that the basic nature of subatomic particles and of light is both (not either/or) wave and particle. The expression of 'waviness' or 'particulateness' depends on the circumstances. At one extreme only particulate properties are expressed while at the other only wave properties are expressed—and in between both wave and particle properties are displayed.

The difficulty in visualising the dual particle/wave nature of the very small stems from the fact that we normally don't encounter this duality in the everyday physical world. However, if we think more generally we can easily identify cases where a characteristic can also express itself in the opposite manifestation. For example, one must sometimes be cruel to be kind.

If you find it difficult to understand what I have been explaining, don't worry. I don't really understand this stuff myself. But, we are in good company—that of Albert Einstein who said: 'Fifty years of conscious brooding have brought me no nearer to the answer to the question—What are light quanta? Nowadays every Tom, Dick and Harry thinks he knows it, but he is mistaken.'

The Origin of Life

The Spontaneous Generation of Life: a History of Ideas

A naturalistic idea—as opposed to a supernaturalistic idea—is testable and therefore resides within the realm of science. There have been only three naturalistic theories of the origin of life since the time of Aristotle. These theories are:

n   the traditional theory of spontaneous generation

n   panspermia

n   chemical evolution.

The current scientific consensus as to the origin of life is the theory of chemical evolution, culminating in the spontaneous eruption of life.

The theory of panspermia (i.e. that pre-formed life was seeded on Earth from elsewhere in the universe) remains a respectable, if minority, opinion. Although the general theory of spontaneous generation was finally disproved over one hundred years ago, it had a long and interesting history which I will outline in this chapter. Interestingly, the modern theory of the origin of life is also a special case of spontaneous generation.

Spontaneous generation is the name that was given to the general idea that life can spontaneously and continually arise from non-living matter—from mud, refuse, etc. The idea also claimed that one form of life could directly change into another form, for example seeds could turn into mice. Spontaneous generation of plants and animals was commonly accepted as a fact until the middle of the seventeenth century. The theory survived until the middle of the nineteenth century in a slightly modified form, with microbes replacing higher forms of life as the end-products of spontaneous generation.

The medieval Church accepted the doctrine of spontaneous generation. St Thomas Aquinas (1225–1274) pronounced on the exact mechanism of spontaneous generation—it was all done by angels acting through the agency of the Sun. The sixteenth century was particularly enthusiastic about spontaneous generation. Jean Baptiste van Helmont (1577–1644), a disciple of Paracelsus (the Father of Modern Medicine) published a well-known method for breeding mice—place grains of wheat in a jar, add an old vest and wait. Two hundred years later Pasteur commented on van Helmont's recipe: 'This proves it is easy to do experiments, but hard to do them flawlessly'. If Pasteur made any comments on St Thomas Aquinas's theoretical work on spontaneous generation, they were not recorded (or perhaps were not repeatable).

The theory of the spontaneous generation of animals finally died during the Renaissance, at the hands of Francesco Redi (1626–1697). Redi was one of the first modern biologists. He was also a physician and a popular poet—a formidable 'Renaissance Man'. Insects were his main scientific interest and his clever and careful experiments brushed aside the convictions of twenty centuries regarding spontaneous generation.

Redi first of all carefully observed what happened when dead eels were allowed to decay in an open box. He noted that the flesh quickly became covered with worms, which gradually increased in size and numbers. Redi described how these worms changed into pupae and finally into adult flies. He carried out many such experiments using the flesh of a wide variety of animals and found that the same thing happened in every case. Redi also noted that, in addition to the worms, the decaying flesh was also peppered with eggs from which the worms hatched. He reasoned that it was most likely that these eggs were dropped onto the meat by flies, and that all the worms found on decaying meat came directly from fly droppings.

Redi tested his hypothesis with an experiment. He divided fresh flesh into two lots. He placed one lot in a flask, which he then sealed. He placed the other lot in a separate flask, which was left open to the air. After a short while the flesh in the open flask became wormy and flies were readily seen entering and leaving the flask. Worms were not seen in the closed flask. In a further refinement of this experiment Redi allowed air to enter both flasks, but he protected one flask with a fine veil that prevented flies (and their accompanying eggs) from entering, while still allowing air to circulate. The other flask was not protected with any veil. No worms developed in the flask protected against the flies, while worms quickly appeared in the unprotected flask.

Redi's account of his experiments was published widely and killed off belief in the spontaneous generation of animals amongst educated people. However, the doctrine of spontaneous generation was revived at another level. About 1675 micro-organisms were discovered by the Dutch microscopist Anton Leeuwenhoek (1632–1723). Microbes are so small and simple that it was widely believed they existed in a grey area between life and non-life. It seemed intuitively 'logical' that they could arise spontaneously as the products of decay. An English clergyman, J. T. Needham (1713–1781), claimed that, for example, mutton gravy, heated to kill all existing micro-organisms and sealed in a vessel with some air, would, after a few days, spontaneously generate new micro-organisms and decompose. These experiments were repeated by the Italian physiologist Spallanzani who showed that, if the flasks were heated after sealing, the contents did not putrefy and nothing grew in the flasks no matter how long they were kept. Needham replied that heating the sealed flasks destroyed some vital element in the air which was necessary for spontaneous generation.

There the matter lay until Louis Pasteur (1822–1895) eventually solved the problem. In a series of technically brilliant experiments, Pasteur closed the long history of the spontaneous generation doctrine. He clearly showed that the 'vital principle' in air responsible for the 'spontaneous' appearance of microbial life in sterilised broths is microbial life itself, hitchhiking on dust particles. Pasteur proved that life can only arise from pre-existing life. The modern theory of the spontaneous origin of life on Earth about three and a half billion years ago is considered to be a unique exception to the principle established by Pasteur.

In one of Pasteur's simplest experiments he placed yeast extract plus sugar into a glass flask and, using a flame, extended the neck of the flask to form a long narrow tube which he bent in various ways, for example into a U-shape. The bore of the tube was very narrow, but open. He next heated the medium in the flask to boiling point for a few minutes and then let the flask cool down. The yeast extract remained sterile indefinitely, even though it was in contact with air.

Pasteur explained that the air in the long narrow neck acts as a buffer, damping down rapid movement of air, so that any dust attempting to enter the flask falls out and is held on the walls of the neck before it gets into the liquid contents of the flask. To demonstrate that the boiled yeast extract would actually support micro-organism growth in the presence of dusty air, Pasteur cut the necks off some flasks and they soon sprouted microbial growths. Pasteur had succeeded in repeating the Redi experiment at the level of the micro-organism.

At that time, between one quarter and one half of patients receiving amputations in British hospitals died, mainly from infections. Joseph Lister (1827–1912) was familiar with the work of Pasteur. He reasoned that if he prevented micro-organisms in the air from reaching incisions in his patients he would lower the incidence of infection. Up until then no special precautions were taken to exclude germs from wounds because it was believed they would be generated spontaneously in the wound anyway. Lister decided to kill bacteria before they reached patients' incisions and he used carbolic acid as an antibacterial agent. He sprayed the surgery and his instruments and he applied carbolic acid to his patients dressings. These measures were quite successful. Antiseptic surgery was born.

Was Life Seeded on Earth from Elsewhere in the Universe?

The idea that life springs on a continual basis from non-living matter (spontaneous generation) was widely believed for over two thousand years— from the time of Aristotle until it was finally disproved by Louis Pasteur in the nineteenth century. The theory of spontaneous generation was smoothly succeeded by the theory of panspermia, i.e. that pre-formed life was seeded on Earth from elsewhere in the universe. The theory of panspermia was later replaced in mainstream science by the theory of chemical evolution. This is now the generally accepted scientific hypothesis to explain the mechanism whereby life spontaneously arose on Earth about three and a half billion years ago. Nevertheless, the theory of panspermia persists as a respectable minority scientific opinion.

When Pasteur conclusively showed that, under present conditions, life can only arise from pre-existing life, there was little point in pondering how life might have first arisen on Earth. At the time, far too little was known about the histories of life, biology and the Earth. Nevertheless, Pasteur's dictum had such a powerful resonance that some scientists proposed the idea that life had no origin, but always existed, just like matter and energy. According to this idea, the origin of life on a planet, previously life-less, could only be effected by seeding pre-formed life onto the planet from elsewhere.

Several well-known nineteenth century physicists approved of the idea of the seeding of life, including William Thompson, who later became Lord Kelvin (1824–1907). The idea was more fully developed in 1908 by Svante Arrhenius (1859–1927), a Swedish chemist. He christened the theory with the name panspermia (from the Greek, meaning 'seeds-all'). Arrhenius proposed a mechanism whereby life could hop from planet to planet. He proposed that biological organisms, such as bacterial spores and viruses, are ejected from planets by electrical forces and propelled through space by the weak pressure of starlight. Such organisms become attached to dust particles in space, thus increasing their mass, and then fall under gravity towards the nearest star, perhaps to land on a planet of that star. A direct consequence of this theory is that all living things in the universe are biochemically related to each other.

One aspect of the theory can be ruled out straight away. Life is not as fundamental as matter and energy and could not have existed from the birth of the universe. Cosmologists tell us that, in the beginning, only hydrogen and a small amount of helium existed. Hydrogen is still the most abundant element in the cosmos, making up over sixty per cent of the mass of the visible universe. The various other elements that exist have been produced in stars, and continue to be produced, by nuclear fusion processes. Since living matter is composed of chemical combinations of many different elements, life cannot be as old as the cosmos.

There is also reason to doubt that spores of life can successfully journey long distances through space. Many scientists believe that any biological organism would be killed in space by lethal radiation—ultraviolet radiation, X-rays and cosmic radiation. These radiations would have a long time to interact with the bacterial spores since interstellar distances, and therefore travel times, are so immense.

On the other hand, experiments have been carried out in which bacterial spores were exposed to intense ultraviolet rays, extreme cold and vacuum conditions, in order to mimic the environment of interstellar space. Some of these studies claimed that, if the spores were carried within the molecular clouds which roam around space, a fraction of the spores could remain viable for many millions of years, perhaps long enough to travel from one solar system to another.

But, on the other hand again, there is evidence that biological spores neither leave our Earth nor enter our vicinity from elsewhere. One would expect the Moon to intercept many particles leaving the Earth and also to intercept biological particles arriving from elsewhere. However, Moon samples brought to Earth by the Apollo mission contained no micro-organisms. Also, tests carried out by the Viking mission to Mars found no detectable biological activity in Martian soil.

Many people will have heard of the proposition put forward by Fred Hoyle, the well known astrophysicist. He claims that over eighty per cent of all interstellar dust grains are bacterial and algal cells. This conclusion is based on the light-absorbing properties of the dust grains. It is estimated that the mass of these grains in our Milky Way Galaxy is equivalent to five million Suns. In other words, space is teeming with life! But why is this life not falling onto the Moon?

Another more recent version of the panspermia theory is called directed panspermia. This theory holds that life was not seeded on Earth by accident, but was sent in interstellar spacecraft by other intelligent beings. The best known directed panspermia hypothesis has been proposed by Francis Crick and Leslie Orgel. Crick and Orgel do not believe that sufficient time was available on the early Earth to allow chemical evolution to produce life. However, they believe that enough time existed between the origin of the universe and four billion years ago (when life first appeared on Earth) for an advanced technological race to have developed elsewhere capable of effecting directed panspermia. Crick and Orgel believe that life originally began elsewhere in the universe in a spontaneous process similar to the conventional scientific explanation for the origin of life on Earth.

Hoyle, Crick and Orgel are all brilliant scientists. Their ideas on panspermia are based on serious considerations and deserve our serious attention.

One issue that gives minor cause for doubt about the conventional scientific explanation for the origin and development of life on Earth is the absolute uniformity of the basic biochemical lifeplan in all living organisms. Almost every conceivable environmental niche on Earth is inhabited by its own form of life—fissures in the deep ocean floor, dry rocks in the deep-freeze of Antarctica, scalding hot springs, and so on. The overall shapes and forms assumed by life are dramatically different—for example, bacteria, jelly-fish, mice, elephants, whales and oak trees. But the basic biochemical plan of the cells of every living organism is pretty much identical. DNA directs the manufacture of protein and proteins carry out the work of the cell. The genetic code of bacteria is essentially identical to the genetic code of President Bill Clinton.

The conventional scientific explanation for this is that life arose in a unique event and in a particular biochemical configuration. All species of life that now inhabit the Earth are descended from that original ancestor and inherit the same basic biochemical lifeplan. However, is it not surprising, in view of the spectacular variations shown by life at other levels, that there is essentially no variation in the basic biochemical plan of life? One possible explanation for this is that life never had any choice in its basic biochemical plan because the basic stock was seeded here from elsewhere in the universe.

The Origin of Life: Did it Begin in a Frozen Ocean?

Many large questions remain to be answered in biology. Perhaps the most fascinating question of all is—how did life first arise on Earth? A dramatic experimental breakthrough was made nearly fifty years ago. The basic insight provided by that famous experiment remains valid, but developments in the meantime have led some to believe that life first began in a very cold ocean under a thick layer of ice, rather than in a completely liquid ocean as originally surmised.

In 1952, Stanley Miller, a young graduate student at the University of Chicago, working under the supervision of the Nobel laureate chemist Harold Urey, carried out an experiment in which he attempted to reproduce the conditions that first produced life on Earth. He connected two flasks with tubing. Into one he put water (the ocean) and into the other a mixture of gases, principally hydrogen, ammonia and methane (the original atmosphere). He passed an electric arc (lightning) through the gases for one week. By this time the water had turned brown and chemical analysis showed that it contained many organic compounds found in biological organisms, including several amino acids. Amino acids are the building blocks of proteins, one of the main components of the living cell.

Since then many experiments have been carried out using various mixtures of gases thought to approximate to the chemically reducing atmosphere of the early Earth, and using other sources of energy, such as ultraviolet light, known to be available on the young planet. In most cases a rich mixture of organic compounds was formed containing many of the basic building blocks of life—'prebiotic soup'.

And so, the following consensus emerged amongst scientists. The building blocks of life were formed as demonstrated in Miller's experiment. The various chemicals in this prebiotic soup interacted and reacted in a form of chemical evolution lasting for millions of years. Eventually information-rich self-replicating molecules arose and, later still, the first living cell.

The insight provided by Miller's 1952 experiment promised that an explanation would quickly emerge as to how events evolved from simple building blocks to the first living cell. However, while progress has been made in this area, it must be admitted that science remains a long way from the answer to this question.

Life began on Earth about three and a half billion years ago, having arisen from prebiotic soup—if we accept the proposal of Urey and Miller. On the face of it, to go from simple building block chemicals to a living cell is an enormously improbable step. Several prominent scientists (such as Francis Crick and Fred Hoyle) have concluded that there wasn't enough time available on the early Earth to allow this development to evolve.

Both Crick and Hoyle have proposed that life began elsewhere in the universe and was subsequently seeded on Earth—panspermia. It is now known that organic compounds and basic building block chemicals found in living organisms are formed on a widespread basis throughout the universe. The Murchison meteorite, which landed in Australia in 1969, contains about eighty amino acids, including at least eight of the twenty amino acids that are present in proteins in organisms on Earth.

The panspermia hypothesis is not widely accepted by scientists. The general consensus remains that life began on Earth by evolving from the primeval prebiotic soup. However, certain difficulties have emerged with the details of this model as it was originally proposed. One problem concerns the composition of the primeval atmosphere.

Urey and Miller originally assumed that the early Earth had a reducing atmosphere, i.e. it favoured chemical reactions that would produce organic compounds. It was thought that the early atmosphere was devoid of oxygen, rich in methane and ammonia, and also contained hydrogen. It is known that the early Earth was violent, riven by electrical storms, suffused with strong ultraviolet light, rocked by volcanic eruptions and bombarded with comets and asteroids. Under such conditions, as Miller's experiment shows, the basic building blocks of life are easily formed.

However, evidence has emerged since the 1950s that the composition of the early atmosphere may have been chemically very different from that previously proposed. Many meteorologists have pointed out that gases such as methane and ammonia are unstable in ultraviolet light and would not persist in the atmosphere. Many atmospheric scientists now favour an atmosphere largely composed of nitrogen and carbon dioxide almost from the very beginning. This atmosphere contained no oxygen and it had much more carbon dioxide than our present atmosphere. The problem with this revised early atmosphere is that, if you repeat Miller's experiment using these gases, nothing happens.

So, if the revised notion of the early atmosphere is right, how could the building blocks of life have been formed? A new proposal to answer this question has come forward from J. Bada (Scripps Institution, University of California) and Stanley Miller and co-workers in which the necessary reducing environment is present in the waters of the ocean, rather than in the gases of the atmosphere. In this scenario it is necessary to have the reaction vessel in the liquid ocean partitioned off temporarily from the atmosphere above. This would happen if the oceans were frozen, but not all the way to the bottom.

The Earth is presently maintained well above freezing temperatures on average because sufficient heat from the Sun is retained close to the Earth by the gases in the atmosphere, keeping the climate temperate—the greenhouse effect. Carbon dioxide is an important greenhouse gas. The Sun that shone on our early Earth four billion years ago was twenty to thirty per cent cooler than at present. The greenhouse effect of the gas mixture in the very early atmosphere may not have been strong enough to compensate for the weak Sun and, consequently, the Earth could have frozen.

The ocean would not have frozen all the way to the bottom. Radioactive decay in the Earth produces heat that flows out into the ocean. Four billion years ago this heat flow was three times greater than now. This heat would have kept the ocean liquid, below a surface ice-sheath about three hundred metres thick. Methane and ammonia could enter the water by bubbling up through vents in the ocean floor. Reaction would then take place in the water to form the basic building block chemicals. The cold temperature of $-2°$ Celsius would prolong the lifespan of the organic molecules and would provide a particularly favourable environment for chemical evolution to occur over millions of years, producing a rich prebiotic soup from which a living cell would eventually emerge.

How did the Earth subsequently unfreeze itself? The Sun at the time was too weak, but cosmic collisions could have provided enough energy. The early Earth was subject to frequent collisions with meteorites, comets, asteroids and miscellaneous debris left over from the formation of the solar system. When such objects hit the Earth, seventy-five per cent of their energy is dissipated at the site of impact and twenty-five per cent heats the atmosphere. An object one hundred kilometres across could have melted all the ice on Earth. Once the ice was melted, the high concentration of carbon dioxide in the early atmosphere, although insufficient to trap enough heat to melt the ice, would have prevented it from freezing again.

This revised scheme is basically very similar to the original scheme proposed by Miller and Urey. It differs in details to accommodate revised ideas of the composition of the early atmosphere. Urey's half-joking remark made in 1953 still applies: 'If God didn't do it this way, he missed a good bet'.

Are We Alone in the Universe?

Speculation about the existence of intelligent life elsewhere in the universe goes back to ancient times when people pondered the night sky, drew imaginary lines between stars and supposed these regions to be populated by gods such as Mars and Jupiter. In the nineteenth and early twentieth centuries there was intense speculation, based on telescopic observations, about the existence of intelligent life on Mars. The possibility of intelligent alien life exerts a powerful grip on the imagination which is expressed in a distinct branch of literature—science fiction. Many films in this genre have been hugely popular, such as 'Close Encounters of the Third Kind' and 'ET'.

No verifiable contact has ever been made with extraterrestrial intelligence, nor have we any proof that such intelligence exists. Nevertheless, many scientists believe it is almost certain that intelligent lifeforms have developed elsewhere in the universe. Each such intelligent civilisation would also realise that it is not unique and, if at a level of development equal to or greater than our own, would make efforts to contact civilisations elsewhere in the universe. This line of reasoning has led to organised scientific efforts in many countries to search for extraterrestrial intelligence (SETI).

In order to assess the probability of life arising elsewhere in the universe it is first necessary to understand the conventional scientific explanation of how life arose and developed on Earth (alternative scenarios can also be envisaged—see the previous chapter, on the origin of life). Living matter is composed of basic chemical building blocks, such as amino acids, sugars and fatty acids. These compounds did not exist on Earth when the planet was formed. It is believed that the early atmosphere of the Earth was composed largely of the gases hydrogen, methane, ammonia and water vapour. Ultraviolet light from the Sun was very strong and massive electrical storms constantly rained down into the oceans. This incubation of electricity, ultraviolet, atmospheric gases and the ocean brought about the synthesis of the basic chemical building blocks of life. These and other chemicals formed and dissolved in the oceans to form a rich chemical soup.

Endless combinations and recombinations between chemicals occurred in the chemical soup over millions of years. New forms, particularly suited to the environmental conditions, were gradually favoured over others—chemical evolution. Eventually certain molecules arose that were capable of replicating themselves and, later, these molecules and others organised themselves into the first living, reproducing cell. New varieties of the cell arose in time; those best suited to the environment flourished while others perished. This was biological evolution through natural selection. This biological evolution proceeded apace, eventually producing the myriad lifeforms that presently populate the Earth, including humankind.

It is implicit in the above scientific scheme that the nature of matter and the laws of physics are such that living forms will inevitably arise, given the right chemical ingredients, environmental conditions and sufficient time. We assume that the laws of physics and the basic nature of matter are the same everywhere in the universe, but how often might these coincide with favourable environmental conditions that would allow living forms to develop?

It is only possible to approach this question on the basis of probability. Our own Milky Way galaxy is vast (100,000 light-years wide) containing hundreds of billions of stars and, presumably, many billions of planets. Beyond our galaxy the universe presumably contains almost unimaginably large numbers of planets. If each planet in the universe is considered as a random throw of the dice, it seems very improbable that the dice has only once turned up amenable conditions for the development of intelligent life. A well-known equation for estimating the probable number of alien civilisations, the Drake Equation, estimates that our own Milky Way galaxy has about four thousand civilisations at a stage of development capable of transmitting messages across space.

It is thought that such alien civilisations would transmit messages across the vastness of space by microwave radio transmission, which travels at the speed of light (186,000 miles per second)—the fastest velocity allowed in the universe by the laws of physics. The SETI programmes in various countries, therefore, use massive radiotelescopes to scan the cosmos for

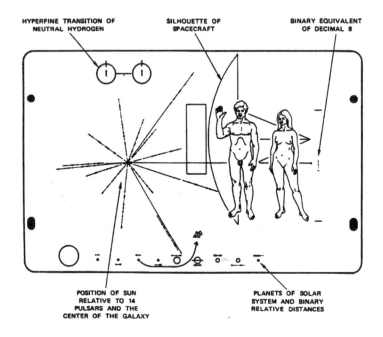

The Interstellar postcard carried on Pioneer 10

intelligent radio messages. No intelligent messages have so far been received, but the listening process has only really just started.

In May 1999, an exciting project called Seti-at-home was launched that allows any member of the public with a PC connected to the Internet to search for extraterrestrial life. If you register with this programme, you will receive data collected by the Arecibo Radio Telescope in Puerto Rico plus software that will analyse the data when you are not using your PC for other work. You can get further information from the website http://setiathome.ssl.berkeley.edu/.

In addition to listening for messages, SETI scientists have also broadcast information into the cosmos about our human civilisation. The first broadcast was made in 1974 from Cornell University's giant radiotelescope transmitter in Arecibo, Puerto Rico. The message contained information that locates our Sun in the galaxy and the Earth in our solar system. There was also a brief description of the human form and composition. The message was beamed at a cluster of stars 25,000 light-years away. So, in 50,000 years we may get a reply!

'Postcard' messages have also been sent into outer space. NASA's Pioneer ten spacecraft, launched in 1972, was designed to fly by the planet Jupiter. However, it was known to have enough energy to continue on and become the first object from our civilisation to leave our solar system to sail forever through space. A plaque was placed aboard the craft detailing various pieces of information about the Earth and humankind. It is curious to think of an alien civilisation finding the spacecraft, perhaps millions of years from now, and pondering over the message on the plaque.

Some scientists argue that SETI programmes are not justified because it is extremely unlikely that life exists anywhere except on Earth. This argument is based on very pessimistic estimations of probability. It seems most unlikely to me, and probably to a majority of scientists, that the Earth is unique, but there is much latitude for debate on this matter. However, even as you read these words, a SETI worker may be receiving the first message.

The Anthropic Principle: is the Universe Specially Designed to Support Life?

Scientists are often impressed by how finely tuned the world is for the existence of life. If any of a large number of fundamental physical properties of the world were slightly different, biological life would be impossible. The observation that we inhabit a world which is uniquely suited to us has led to the development of a scientific principle called the anthropic principle. This principle asserts that we see the universe the way it is because we exist. There are two forms of the anthropic principle—a weak form and a strong form. Most scientists find the weak anthropic principle to be a useful methodological principle, but few scientists believe in the strong form of the principle. Others claim that the anthropic principle is not a scientific principle at all, but is just an irritating tautology. The principle is lucidly described in *Theories of Everything* by J. D. Barrow (Clarendon Press, 1991).

The weak anthropic principle recognises that the fact of human existence requires certain conditions to be met regarding the past and the present structure of the universe. In other words, the conditions we observe in the universe must be such that allowed carbon-based beings like ourselves to arise and evolve within a certain time-frame. This time-frame must reside in a window of opportunity bounded at the late end by the death of the Sun and, at the early end, by the requirement that the elements that compose our bodies must be present. Therefore, when intelligent observers find that the conditions in the universe are suitable for their existence, this is no reason for surprise or wonder.

One application of the weak anthropic principle is to 'explain' why the universe is about fifteen billion years old. Living systems on Earth are made from carbon-based molecules in which carbon is combined with hydrogen, nitrogen, phosphorous and oxygen. The cosmologists tell us that, in the beginning, there was only hydrogen and a little helium. All of the heavier elements in nature were subsequently bred in the interiors of the stars by nuclear processes. At the ends of their lives, many stars explode and spew the heavier elements into space, where they become incorporated into molecules, planets and, eventually, people. The process whereby the biological building blocks of life are produced is long and slow. It took about ten billion years from the Big Bang origin of the universe before our solar system was formed. Another billion years passed before life began on Earth. Life subsequently evolved for about four billion years. And so, this is why the universe is about fifteen billion years old.

The weak anthropic principle mainly concerns itself with large-scale observed properties of the universe. Strong versions of the anthropic principle attempt to account for the fundamental constants of the universe and assert that the universe must have those properties that allow life to develop. There are many fundamental constants, including the force of gravity, the charge on the electron and the ratio of photons (basic units of light) to nuclear

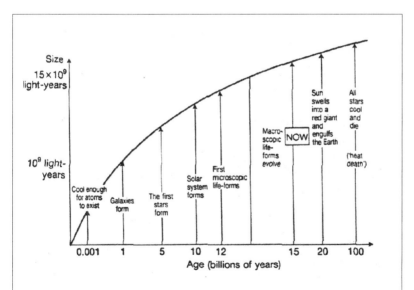

The universe has been expanding with time from its beginning in the Big Bang. Life on Earth could only begin and develop in our universe in the window bounded on the early side by the birth of the stars and on the late side by the death of all stars of the universe.

particles (protons and neutrons). It has often been observed that the force of gravity, for example, is set at an ideal level for the existence of life. If the force of gravity were slightly higher the stars would burn more rapidly. Consequently our Sun would burn itself out in one billion years, instead of its present ten billion year lifespan, and this would not allow enough time for the human species to evolve. On the other hand, if the force of gravity were slightly less than it is, the Sun would burn more slowly and the temperature would be cooler. Consequently, the temperature on Earth would be too low to sustain life as we know it.

The ratio of photons to nuclear particles is also most convenient. This ratio plays a vital role in determining the rate at which the cosmos expands. If the ratio were significantly higher than it is, the universe would expand so quickly that the stars and galaxies probably would not have formed, and consequently there would be no place for life to inhabit.

The strong form of the anthropic principle leads to the conclusion that there may be a large number of alternative universes, each with its own configuration and possibly its own laws of science. In most of these universes conditions will not be right for the development of life, and consequently these places contain no scientists or philosophers to contemplate them and to ask questions such as 'why is the universe the way we see it?'.

Before the work of Nicolas Copernicus (1473–1543), humankind was assigned a position of pre-eminent importance in the natural world. The universe was thought to be centred on humans. After Copernicus everything changed—humankind was denied any special cosmological status. But now, if you accept the anthropic principle, a limited degree of status is again conferred on humankind. The anthropic principle would not restore pre-Copernican status, but it does accord some privilege to mankind.

It could be argued that the anthropic principle is just as anthropocentric as cosmological thinking before the time of Copernicus. The strong form of the anthropic principle seems to rule out the possibility of the existence of life that is not broadly similar to life as we know it. This may not be sensible. After all, there are several examples of accomplished scientists who have credibly speculated on forms of life, radically different from life on Earth, in works of science-fiction, such as Fred Hoyle in *The Dark Cloud* (1957). One can imagine such intelligent alien lifeforms contemplating their surroundings in other universes—and devising their own anthropic principle to rule out a possibility of intelligent life in a universe such as ours because the constants of nature in our universe would not support a lifeform such as theirs!

It is important to point out that the anthropic principle (at least in the weak form) is not a causal explanation—it does not claim that the existence of life causes the constants of nature to have their observed values. The principle acts more to constrain the features of the universe than to explain them. In other words, if the nature of the universe differed markedly from what we see, we would not be here to comment on it.

Albert Einstein had the happy knack of making comments that are memorable and hence frequently quoted. At one stage he said that the reason he studied physics was to discover 'if God had any choice in the way He made the universe'. Physicists really do not know yet if there was any choice in this matter. However, some believe that the theory of quantum mechanics leaves room for choice. The origin of the universe involved quantum processes and such processes determine the probability of events, but not the events themselves. It could therefore be argued that choices did exist, many were acted on and there may be many universes created in accordance with laws that allow for randomness in the fundamental constants. These fundamental constants may differ from universe to universe, leaving many universes unfit for life. In such a scenario the anthropic principle makes sense.

On the other hand, if the physical laws reigning at the birth of the universe allowed for only one set of values for the physical constants, then the anthropic principle would seem to be unnecessary. In this scenario the universe is absolutely determined from the start and the evolution of life is guaranteed.

Of course, there is another way of thinking that is a rival to the anthropic principle, and this can be called the God principle. This states that the reason we find the universe tailor-made for our existence is because it was deliberately designed for our existence. God created the universe the way it is as a home for intelligent life. Science can only deal with natural explanation and therefore cannot subscribe to the God principle. Religion responds to the unique fitness of the world for life with the God principle—science responds with the anthropic principle. A cynic might remark that the anthropic principle is the closest some atheists can get to God.

Dinosaur tracks made about 135 million years ago in soft sand that was later converted into hard rock. The tracks were found near Fort Worth, Texas, and were made by two dinosaurs, a large four-footed creature and a smaller two-footed creature. The human figure in the top right-hand of the picture indicates the scale of the prints.

The Theory of Evolution

The Explanatory Power of the Theory of Evolution

The theory of evolution is the central unifying theory in biology. Without this theory there would be no scientific framework to explain the vast accumulation of observations that have been made of the biological world. The theory of evolution by natural selection was a major revolutionary change in thinking when introduced in the middle of the last century. It had widespread implications which many people are still unable to accept.

Very briefly, the modern scientific understanding of the origin of life and its subsequent evolution is as follows. The basic biochemical molecules on which living cells are based arose naturally from simple precursors on the ancient Earth about four billion years ago. These biochemicals eventually and spontaneously organised themselves into the first living, replicating, biological cell about three and a half billion years ago.

The information that controls the cell is contained in the biochemical DNA in the form of a linear code, based on four letters. This coded information is faithfully replicated and passed on to the cell's progeny when the cell divides. The cell replication process is very accurate but, nevertheless, small errors (mutations) creep in over time. Most of these mutations are harmful, produce defective progeny that fail to reproduce and so the mutations are thereby eliminated from the stock. However, some mutations confer a selective advantage on the particular individuals involved, allowing them to adapt better to the environment and therefore to reproduce more successfully than their fellows. In this way the new favourable mutations spread throughout the population. The theory of evolution proposes that such gradual changes, sieved through this process of natural selection and operating over billions of years, slowly but surely developed the myriad forms of biological life on Earth today, including humankind.

There is a huge amount of experimental and observational evidence to support the theory of evolution. At this stage, in conventional biological science, it is pretty much unanimously accepted that biological evolution is a fact. However, there is still considerable debate about various aspects of the details of the mechanism of evolution.

In my opinion, the weakest link in the explanatory chain of evolutionary developments that I outlined above is the first step in which the primordial biochemicals organised themselves into the first living, self-replicating cell. I cannot see how the first living cell spontaneously arose. Of course, neither can anybody else—the mechanism is presently unknown. Some people have concluded that this step could not have evolved on Earth in the time available. They propose therefore that pre-formed life was seeded on Earth from outer space. For my part, I am prepared to patiently await the development of a scientific mechanism to explain how life spontaneously arose on Earth from non-living biochemicals. If a scientific mechanism is not forthcoming within a reasonable amount of time, then science will have to think again. In that event, the conventional theory of the evolution of life would have to begin with the first living cell, and not with the primordial chemical soup. The only alternative would be to paper over a gap in a scientific scheme with an act of faith!

The theory of evolution has had a profound effect on our psychological orientation to the world. Prior to this theory, humans could legitimately view themselves as special creatures sitting on the pinnacle of creation, chosen to fill this role from the very outset. According to the theory of evolution, humankind is simply another animal species recently evolved from an ape-like ancestor. It also follows from the theory of evolution that our highest and most prized capacities—self-consciousness, language and culture—became established by natural selection because they conferred a procreative advantage. Also, there is no obvious place for God in the scheme of evolution—you simply pour in certain chemicals and the right environmental conditions at one end of the scheme, wait a sufficiently long period of time and the present biological world emerges naturally at the other end.

Religion is a powerful comfort to people. It sets out to explain why we exist and how we should live, and it provides the prospect of a spiritual after-life when the body dies. Belief in God is central to Christian religions. While belief in God must rely largely on faith, this will be ultimately unsatisfactory if such a belief can be shown to be unreasonable on the basis of ordinary logic. If one can show that the existence of God is reasonable from a logical consideration of the nature of the world, then so much the better.

Traditionally there were several respectable logical arguments for the existence of God. One of the best known is the argument from design, formulated in the eighteenth century by the Protestant theologian William Paley. This held that intelligent purposeful design implies a designer. Such design is abundantly evident in the natural world, therefore this world was designed by an intelligence, and this intelligence is God.

The argument from design was good in its time. However, in the theory of evolution a mechanism is proposed that allows design to arise by the unconscious mechanism of natural selection. The designs that are selected are those that can live most efficiently in their natural environments. There is no need to invoke a Creator to explain biological design.

The fact that the theory of evolution proposes a mechanism with no need for God has naturally upset many religious denominations. The more fundamentalist the religious persuasion, the greater is the upset, and such denominations are bitterly opposed to the theory of evolution. There are strengths and weaknesses in a fundamentalist position. One obvious weakness is an inflexibility that prevents reasonable accommodation to developments in knowledge. It is nice to have logical arguments in natural theology to support positions of faith. When these arguments are demolished or greatly weakened by advances in objective knowledge, the only reasonable approach is to replace the old arguments with better ones based on more up-to-date reasoning. Indeed, why can't religion evolve just as the biological world can? The Christian God seems to have no problem with the idea of an evolving religion—compare the New Testament to the Old Testament.

The function of science is to provide natural explanations for how the natural world works. The scientific method has long since proved that it is well capable of doing this. On several notable occasions religion has come off worst when it has denied the validity of new knowledge introduced by science. It seems to me that fundamentalist creationism is now in the process of repeating this mistake. Surely a simple way forward for religion in this debate is simply to say that matter seems to be intrinsically endowed with properties that allow it to organise, replicate and evolve the complex biological structures that we see on Earth today, and that this is God's will.

Evolution, a Disturbing Idea

Of all the topics that I write on, the one that arouses most reaction is evolution. Some people find the concept deeply disturbing. At the heart of this disturbance is the fear that, if evolution is true, everything in the world is devoid of higher meaning. That scenario is simply too bleak and barren for many people to accept and, consequently, they are bitterly opposed to the theory of evolution. But, in my opinion, there is no need to take this pessimistic black and white approach to the matter.

Darwin's and Wallace's theory of evolution by natural selection (1858) did indeed change things utterly. Prior to that it was pretty much universally accepted that the totality of things could be arranged in a hierarchy from top to bottom in the order: God, mind, design, order, chaos, nothingness. It was accepted that all movement of effect in that hierarchy was from higher elements downwards. Then, along came Darwin and Wallace to propose that things actually move in the opposite direction—order can arise out of chaos, design can arise out of order, mind can arise out of design. Darwin and Wallace further proposed a credible mechanism—natural selection—to explain how these changes occur.

Darwin set out to explain the relationship between the different species of life and how these species change over time. His conclusion was that existing forms of life have slowly arisen, through natural selection, from somewhat different forms by a process of gradual modification. Natural selection is the process whereby nature unconsciously favours the reproduction of those individuals who display characteristics that better suit them to their environment than their fellows (who do not display these characteristics). In this way, slowly emerging changes in an organism are naturally selected and this unconscious process produces organisms 'designed' to live efficiently and effectively in the environment.

In his book *The Descent of Man*, Darwin makes it clear that humankind also arose through evolution. In other words, our most prized possession, the self-conscious mind, is the product of unconscious natural selection. This was the most radical proposal imaginable at the time and, to this day, many people cannot accept it. Even Alfred Russell Wallace, who was the co-discoverer of the principle of evolution by natural selection, could not take matters this far. Later in life, he exempted human consciousness from the general scheme of evolution.

I appreciate why many people find it instinctively unpalatable to think that the human mind arose out of the unconscious selection of random changes. Humans are part of nature, but are also obviously very different from the rest of nature. We are self-conscious, we can reason, we have language and culture. It is much more palatable to think that we have a spark of the Divine—that we are connected upwards rather than effected from below.

Many people fear and despise evolution because of its perceived knock-on implications. They feel that, if evolution is true, there is no place for God and there is no preordained purpose in the world; if evolution is true, there are no absolute rights and wrongs and codes of morality become, at best, guidelines to ensure efficient behaviour; if evolution is true, there is no compelling reason for people to be good; if evolution is true, codes of civilised behaviour will inevitably degenerate and civilisation will eventually fall into chaos.

Natural theology produced several 'proofs' for the existence of God. The best of these proofs was the argument from design. This pointed to the sophisticated design that is obvious in the biological world. Where design exists there must be a designer—and that designer is God. Before the theory of evolution, that argument made sense. However, Darwin and Wallace knocked the legs from under it by showing that natural selection can produce design. But while this invalidates the traditional argument from design, it does not disprove the existence of God.

Is it possible to have it both ways—to believe both in evolution and in a God by whose will the world exists and operates? In my opinion, the answer is yes. I am a Christian and I also believe in evolution. My belief in God does not rest to any significant extent on identifying gaps in nature that science cannot explain and invoking God to account for these gaps. I am content that science should go on uncovering mechanisms that explain the natural world. Nevertheless, I think that the basic material (consisting of quarks, electrons and so on) of which the universe is made is so wonderful as to make it not unreasonable to think that it exists by the will of God.

According to the picture provided by science, the universe has bootstrapped its way by natural means all the way from hydrogen in the beginning to Einstein in the twentieth century. It remains to be demonstrated that several huge steps along the way, such as the origin of life and the development of consciousness, occurred by purely natural means, but it is not unlikely that this will eventually be demonstrated. There is no objective evidence that God interferes with the natural unfolding of the world through the operation of the laws of nature. This would mean that the entire world developed naturally to its present state because of the nature of the basic fabric of the universe. In that event we must stand in awe at the amazing potential built into the basic stuff of the universe and ask how can this be so?

Science provides natural explanations for natural phenomena. It is not competent to investigate the supernatural. Neither should we look to science to provide us with moral or ethical codes, although science can provide information useful in part in forming such codes. God is, by definition, supernatural. Belief in God (faith) results from one's response, as a whole human being, to religious teachings and to the experience of living in the world. Science and religion occupy different spheres, but there is not necessarily conflict between the two.

It is very unwise to use gaps in existing understanding of the world as 'proof' of the existence of God. Such evidence can only stand until a natural explanation arises. It seems to me that the existence of God is not a thing that can ever be proved. If there is no God, this is obviously true. If there is a God, and if this ever became self-evident, it would remove the need for faith and for the sensible exercise of free will on our part to believe or to reject belief. The lack of objective rational certainty in this matter, coupled with the existence of just enough evidence for God, seems to be an essential element that validates the faith of humans, as free agents, in a God, whose nature we dimly reflect and in whose direction we aspire to move.

Biological Adam and Eve

The question of where and when our modern human species *Homo sapiens sapiens* began is not yet finally settled. The preponderance of fossil evidence indicates an African origin for modern humans, but this has been vigorously disputed. In recent years, the 'Out of Africa' hypothesis has been strongly supported by a biochemical investigation of genetic material in living cells. An important biochemical investigation in the 1980s traced an ancestral line from modern humans back to a single woman who lived in Africa about 200,000 years ago. Other evidence recently published provides evidence for a male ancestor who also lived about 200,000 years ago.

The earliest human ancestor to diverge from apes, seen in the fossil record, is *Australopithecus afarensis*. In the early 1970s a famous female skeleton of this species, nicknamed Lucy, was unearthed in central Ethiopia. Lucy lived between three and four million years ago. She was less than four feet tall, walked on two legs, had long arms, massive jaws and a small brain (450 cc). About three million years ago, Lucy's kind diverged into two lines of descent, one of which, a million years later, gave rise to the genus *Homo*. The first hominid, *Homo habilis*, lived between two and one and a half million years ago. *Homo habilis* was still of small physique but had a larger brain case (700 cc) than Lucy. About one and a half million years ago, *Homo habilis* evolved into the larger brained (850 cc) *Homo erectus*.

Homo erectus was probably the first hominid to migrate from Africa. Fossils of archaic *Homo sapiens*, the first human subspecies, have been found in Europe, Asia and Africa. It is assumed that these early people descended from *Homo erectus* in various parts of the world simultaneously. The brain of modern humans is about 1,400 cc. *Homo erectus* was eventually succeeded world-wide by the modern subspecies *Homo sapiens sapiens*, whose oldest fossil remains, found in Africa, are about 120,000 years old—80,000 years older than any found in Europe or Asia. This, together with other archaeological evidence, suggests that modern humans developed from a single isolated population of archaic *Homo sapiens* in Africa and then spread out all over the world.

Our bodies are composed of cells and every cell is controlled by its hereditary (genetic) material, which is mainly located in the nucleus of the cell. The genetic material is composed of DNA which contains linear coded information that controls most aspects of the cell's activity. It is also the hereditary material that is passed on to daughters of the cell when the cell divides. The code consists of four letters and is read in blocks of three successive letters. The most important information in the DNA is divided into chunks called genes.

Over long periods, small changes (mutations) occur in the coded hereditary information. It was realised in the 1950s that it is possible to tell how far apart two species are in evolutionary terms (i.e. how long since they both diverged from a common ancestor) by comparing differences in the coded information in a particular gene between the two species.

Almost all the genetic material in the cell is contained in the cell nucleus. Half of this genetic material was originally donated by the father and half by the mother, when a sperm cell from the father united with an egg cell from the mother. Cells also contain hereditary material other than that contained in the cell nucleus. Cells contain organelles called mitochondria, which generate most of the cell's energy. Each mitochondrion has its own DNA.

The sperm consists of a head and a tail and is much smaller than an egg cell. The head of the sperm contains the sperm cell's nucleus and very little else. The tail propels the sperm cell on its journey to the egg. The tail contains a special locomotion apparatus and some mitochondria to provide energy. When the sperm reaches the egg, it is engulfed, thereby fertilising the egg. Mitochondria that enter the egg from the sperm are destroyed by the egg. The fertilised egg now divides and eventually forms the new individual, all of whose mitochondria have been inherited from the mother only.

In the 1980s, a world-wide survey of mitochondrial DNA sequences was carried out. The racial types sampled were African, Asian, European, New Guinean and Australian. The results showed that all groups could trace their ancestry back to a single woman who lived in Africa about 200,000 years ago. This is powerful corroboratory evidence to support the archaeological evidence that modern humans first arose in Africa at that time.

The discovery of the biological African Eve is not a scientific validation of the biblical Adam and Eve story. The existence of the African Eve does not mean that other women were not alive and reproducing at the same time. It merely means that, in the case of the descendants of all the other women from that time to the present day, there was at least one generation without female offspring to pass on the mitochondrial DNA.

In each cell nucleus, except sex cells, the hereditary material is present in the form of twenty-three sets of chromosomes. One set comes from the father and one set from the mother. Sex is determined by the X and Y sex chromosomes. Females contain two X chromosomes, and males contain an X and a Y chromosome. When sex cells (eggs and sperm) are formed, the sets of chromosomes are divided into their individual chromosomes and each sex cell receives twenty-three individual chromosomes and not twenty-three sets. Each egg cell contains an X chromosome, but half of the sperm cells will contain X chromosomes and half will contain Y chromosomes. If an X sperm fertilises an egg the offspring will be female; if a Y sperm fertilises an egg the offspring will be male. Since maleness is exclusively inherited via the Y chromosome, analysis of codes in this chromosome allows the tracing of ancestry through male inheritance in the same way as ancestry was traced through female descent by analysing mitochondrial DNA. Such a study was recently published and provides evidence for a biological Adam who also existed approximately 200,000 years ago. The same remarks apply regarding the comparison of biological Adam to biblical Adam as were already made for biological Eve/biblical Eve.

It is very difficult and slow to reconstruct human evolutionary history relying solely on fossil evidence. Indeed, because of the massive difficulties involved here, it is doubtful if these traditional methods could ever unravel the full evolutionary story. In the future, it seems certain that modern techniques of molecular biology in analysing the genetic content of living cells will play an increasingly important part in this story.

Man the Hunter or Man the Scavenger?

The vast majority of people would take considerable pride in being able to identify personages of eminence in their ancestral lines. Conversely, who would not be bothered if he found the perches on the ancestral tree bedecked with villains?

Such personal feelings are mirrored on a large scale when humanity reflects on its own ancestry. About one hundred and forty years ago, Darwin and Wallace published their revolutionary theory of evolution by natural selection. One of the proposals of this theory is that humankind's immediate ancestor was an ape-like creature. While the theory was warmly welcomed by many biologists and other scientists capable of appreciating the powerful evidence on which it stands, it also generated widespread controversy and opposition. The opposition was engendered, at least in part, by the general distaste felt about the idea of being 'descended from an ape'. The Bishop of Oxford must have felt he was 'getting off a cracker' on behalf of many people when he asked Thomas Huxley (a staunch defender of Darwin's theory) in a famous public debate: 'Is it through his grandfather or his grandmother that Dr Huxley claims descent from an ape?'

Nowadays the general validity of Darwin's theory is widely accepted. Darwin envisaged that hunting was a major activity of the male members of early humankind (hominids). These men would sally forth from base camps and hunt, armed only with sharp pointed sticks and sharp stone implements. They successfully competed for prey against other predators using their intelligence and speed. After a successful hunt the killed animals were dismembered and brought back to base camp for sharing with the main group. The women of the group mostly stayed around base camp. Many would be pregnant, others nursing babies or minding small children. The women also found time to gather a wide variety of nutritious berries, nuts and tubers that, by and large, formed the staple diet for the entire group.

This concept of Man the Hunter has always exerted a powerful grip on the imagination. The noble savage, taking from nature just enough to satisfy his needs and bravely using his wit and speed to compete with other predators, is an attractive idea with which it is easy to identify. However, recent evidence paints a different picture of the lifestyle of early man.

A powerful recent criticism of the traditional picture of Man the Hunter is that the details of this picture are too closely informed by the practices of present day hunter–gatherer societies. The habits of such present-day tribes must surely differ considerably from those of early man. Modern hunter–gatherers are larger in size than early man; they share their environments with fewer large competitors; they use fire; they often keep domesticated animals, such as dogs, to help in hunting, and they generally display sophisticated ingenuity in coping with stark and primitive conditions. The modern argument holds that it is wrong, indeed racist, to assume that modern 'primitive' tribes, many of whom operate a hunter–gatherer society similar to that previously described for Man the Hunter, are simply unaltered relics of the past. The habits of early man were most likely very different from modern tribes.

The first fossil evidence of early man was unearthed at Neander in Germany in 1856. Neanderthal Man lived 35,000 to 100,000 years ago, and although generally considered to be a separate species (*Homo neanderthalensis*) from ourselves (*Homo sapiens*), nevertheless showed great similarities to modern humans. Each subsequent major find of hominid fossils was of increasingly greater age—a major find in the 1970s in Ethiopia and Tanzania yielding remains of hominids who lived between three and four million years ago and classed by many scientists as a species ancestral to all later hominids, including modern man. The fact that fossil remains (of increasing age) have been successfully discovered, and the fact that the first remains found—Neanderthal Man—were so similar to modern man, has biased anthropological research in favour of seeking similarities rather than differences between ourselves and our early ancestors.

Research by Professor Pat Shipman, Johns Hopkins University (and others), on fossil remains between one and a half and two million years old found in Tanzania is yielding a new picture of our early ancestors. Marks on fossilised animal bones found together with the hominid bones have microscopic characteristics that allow them to be classified either as arising from the action of an animal carnivore, e.g. a tiger, or from the use of sharp stone cutting tools used by early man. Also, if both types of mark are present at the same spot, careful scrutiny can tell which mark was made first.

An analysis was made of the anatomical locations of stone tool marks on the animal bones. The distribution of the marks was markedly different from the patterns found on bones of animals butchered by modern hunter–gatherers. Many of the marks were found in 'illogical' places such as the lower parts of animals' legs where there is little or no meat. Few marks were found on bones near major joints where experience with modern tribes shows there are many marks made when the animal is dismembered prior to transportation. Also, in many cases it was seen that, in places where carnivore teeth marks and stone cutting marks coincided, the teeth marks were made first.

All of this evidence is inconsistent with a hunting lifestyle but it does fit a scavenging habit. In other words, our earliest ancestors, instead of directly hunting their own prey, watched and waited on their chance to pick up scraps remaining after other hunting species were finished with their kill. Many of these scraps would be the lean pickings on lower limb bones. The upright stance of the early hominids may have been somewhat accelerated in its development by the scavenging lifestyle. It is particularly suitable mechanically for covering wide areas efficiently while looking for opportunities, and is also particularly good for allowing careful and detailed searches of limited chosen areas.

People are comfortable with the idea of Man the Hunter who seems brave and confident in dealing with his environment. At worst one can identify with him on the basis that 'he was poor but he was honest'. On the other hand, Man the Scavenger seems to lack confidence, to lead a fearful and furtive existence. He is a difficult model to identify with—not nearly 'macho' enough. I must say that I have no difficulty in entertaining the warmest feelings towards the poor devil, who seems to have made the best of difficult circumstances. Evidently the strategy was eminently successful. The proof of this is that I am here writing about it and you are here reading about it.

What Form will Future Human Evolution Take?

It is probably not a matter that often preoccupies you, but it can be fascinating to ponder the future path of human evolution. We know quite a lot about past stages in the evolution of life and this gives some basis from which to peer into the future. However, predictions about the long-term future must remain highly speculative. The area is not beloved of funding agencies so not much is written on the subject. The American biologist Lynn Margulis is an exception. She has thought creatively on this matter and concludes that the long-term future for humanity is to merge with its technological creations to form a new species, hardy enough to colonise the galaxy.

The Earth was formed about five billion years ago. Many scientists believe that the atmosphere of the early Earth was probably composed principally of the gases ammonia, methane, hydrogen and water vapour. Electrical storms and volcanic eruptions were common, and fairly intense ultraviolet radiation reached the surface of the Earth from the Sun. This combination of gases, radiation, electrical discharge, pressure and heat resulted in the synthesis of the chemical building blocks of life—amino acids, sugars, fatty acids and bases (basic components of the genetic material RNA and DNA).

These various chemicals accumulated in the shallow seas of the time, combining and recombining with each other over a period of millions of years (chemical evolution) until eventually self-replicating molecules (ribonucleic acid—RNA) developed. RNA molecules could direct the synthesis of another important class of polymeric (made of many small monomer molecules, joined together) chemicals called proteins. Eventually, a more precise and stable form of self-replicating molecule developed—deoxyribonucleic acid (DNA)—whose information content could be transcribed to RNA, which could in turn direct the synthesis of protein. Eventually these various classes of molecules became enclosed in fatty membranes and about three and a half billion years ago we had the birth of the first living cell organised on the same basic biochemical plan that operates in present-day cells.

The first living cell was a primitive form of bacterium—a little sphere enclosed by membrane about two millionths of a metre in diameter. The process of biological evolution now began, leading eventually to all the lifeforms that inhabit the planet today.

Life began as a simple unicellular form, with an outside membrane but no internal membranes. We call this form of life prokaryotic. The cells of all higher animals and plants (eukaryotic cells) are much larger (fifty millionths of a metre in diameter) than bacterial cells and they have an elaborate system of internal membranes. Eukaryotic cells apparently developed from prokaryotic cells when one prokaryotic cell invaded another, without killing it, and established a symbiotic relationship which eventually became permanent. Eukaryotic cells contain much more genetic information than prokaryotic cells and have the capacity to do unique things, such as form large multicellular organisms. Eventually, about four hundred million years ago, multicellular life left the sea and mounted the land in the form of plants and animals.

The human brain and nervous system is a recent innovation. Less than two million years ago *Homo habilis* and *Homo erectus* appeared and it has only been little more than fifty thousand years since their descendants, *Homo sapiens sapiens*, originated in the Old World. By co-operating together, and with the aid of warm clothes and dwellings, they quickly covered the globe.

For the past two hundred years humanity has been producing machines at an accelerating rate. In the developed world human population numbers are stabilising but the reproduction rates of machines are increasing. In 1984, the robot population of the USA grew by thirty per cent whereas the human population grew by about two per cent. In many ways machines are also much more capable and powerful and change form at a much greater pace than mammals. Machines can outperform humans at many tasks, can survive in a much wider range of environments and can be powered on a diverse range of energy sources—from combustion to nuclear energy.

Machines show many characteristics of a successful new living species, such as large size, rapid rate of mutation, aggressive reproductive rates etc. What about the ability to reproduce? Robots are presently used to make other machines (e.g. motor cars)—they could also make other robots. As time goes on, increasingly smarter robots are being made. I recently heard a professor of cybernetics declare that he has made robots with intelligence equivalent to that of a wasp and he foresees robots with intelligence surpassing that of humans. It is true, of course, that machines are not alive in the biological sense, i.e. they are not based on carbon and guided by genetic information in DNA. However, since machines are devised by human ingenuity, and humans are carbon and DNA based, there is a sense in which machines are also based on carbon and DNA.

Margulis broadly defines technology as the means whereby living systems maintain and advance themselves. She notes that every increase in complexity in the evolution of life is accomplished by subsuming the existing level into the new more complex level. Thus, the mechanism for making the first biological polymer molecules was incorporated as an essential aspect into the first living cell. These first simple cell types became essential components of the more complex eukaryotic cell. Eukaryotic cells in turn associated with each other to become subservient but co-operating units in whole multicellular organisms.

And that is where we stand today. It would be quite in keeping with this line of development for the next stage of human evolution to involve the co-mingling of humanity with its machine technology to form a hybrid species. Granted, this would seem to be a strange fruit on the tree of life, but does it strain the imagination any more than the commonly accepted scientific consensus that a living reproducing cell developed out of a chemical stew? Also, of course, we are already familiar with several examples of the incorporation of mechanical devices into the body, such as artificial hips and limbs and dentures.

There are pressing practical reasons why evolution might develop along the lines suggested by Margulis. Life as we know it cannot survive indefinitely on Earth. Our Sun has a lifespan of only about ten billion years. In five billion years' time the Sun will have used up all the hydrogen fuel in its core and will expand into a red giant and radiate immense heat, evaporating our oceans, melting rocks and destroying the atmosphere. It will then shrink hundreds of times, eventually becoming a tiny spent dwarf star. Only life that has escaped our solar system will survive.

Our present human bodies are adapted to the benign conditions of Earth. We can only tolerate a narrow range of temperature and pressure and we are irreversibly damaged by higher radiation levels. It is likely that most parts of our galaxy are very inhospitable to the physical human condition. We have to leave the Earth eventually anyway, and we have already begun to explore our solar system and beyond. Our prospects of successfully colonising the galaxy would be greatly enhanced if we had much tougher bodies. Our long-term future form could well be a robotic skeleton, composed of tough metal and plastic parts, controlled by our biological nervous system.

Modern Genetics

The Work of Gregor Mendel, the Father of Genetics

This year marks the 177th anniversary of the birth of the great Austrian scientist-monk, Gregor Mendel, who is venerated as the father of modern genetics.

Mendel was born in 1822 of peasant parents in Moravia (now part of the Czech Republic). He displayed a great love of learning in school. He studied for a short period at the Institute of Olmutz, but had to leave for financial reasons. He became an Augustinian monk at the monastery at Brno. He studied mathematics and natural history in Vienna to become a schoolmaster teaching science in high school in Brno. In his spare time he studied the results of crossing different varieties of garden peas.

Mendel's interest in plant breeding had been sparked by observations of the results of the hybridisation of ornamental plants to produce new varieties. He noted the regularity of the results and he wondered what would happen if the hybrids were crossed to produce further generations. Garden peas

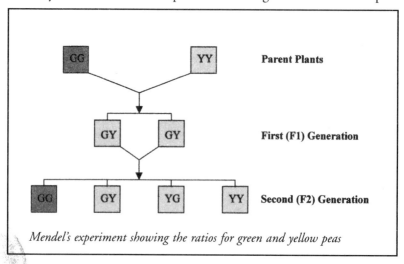

Mendel's experiment showing the ratios for green and yellow peas

were available in pure-breeding varieties. They reproduce sexually and the reproductive organs are enclosed within the petals so that self-pollination (self-fertilisation) normally takes place. However, the plants can easily be artificially cross-pollinated. Mendel studied twenty-two different varieties in experiments extending over eight years.

To illustrate some of the results achieved by Mendel, let us consider his studies concerning the position of the pea-flowers on the stem. Mendel used two varieties of pure-breeding plants. In one variety the flowers always had an axial distribution, i.e. along the main stem. In the other variety the flowers always had a terminal distribution, i.e. bunched at the top of the stem. Mendel cross-pollinated these two varieties and examined the progeny—called the F1 generation. The parent plants are called the P1 generation.

The male and female sex organs of the same plant are enclosed within the flower. The tip of the male organ is called the anther and produces the male sex cell—the pollen. The pistil (female organ) produces the egg cell. The cross-pollination was carried out as follows. Mendel removed the anthers of an immature flower of one variety (i.e. terminal or axial flowers) and covered the flower with a small bag to prevent stray pollen from other plants from landing. When the pistil was mature, Mendel transferred pollen from the alternative variety and again covered it. Mendel found that all the plants in the F1 generation were of the axial flower variety.

In an effort to find what had happened to the hereditary factor for terminal flowers, Mendel allowed self-pollination of the F1 plants to produce second generation (F2) plants. In this generation he found that some of the plants were of the terminal flower variety. The ratio of plants in the F2 generation with axial flowers to plants with terminal flowers was 3 to 1 (actually 3.14 to 1).

Mendel reasoned that there are two factors in each plant for flower position, but only one of the two factors is carried by a pollen grain or an egg. When pollination occurs, the number of factors is restored to two. The pure-breeding P1 plants with axial flowers contains two factors for the axial position. The pure-breeding P1 plants with terminal flowers contain two factors for the terminal position. The plants in the F1 generation contained both factors, but all of these plants had axial flowers. Therefore the factor for axial position must be dominant over the factor for terminal position, which Mendel termed a recessive factor.

When F1 generation pollen grains and eggs are formed, some carry the factor for axial flower position and some the factor for terminal position. These plants were allowed to self-fertilise and this produced a random mixture of the two factors. Some seeds got two factors for axial position, some got a factor of each kind, and some got two factors for terminal flowers. Mendel calculated by mathematical probability that one quarter of F2 plants would be of the first kind, one half of the second kind, and one quarter of the third kind. The factor for axial flowers is dominant, therefore the first two groups have axial flowers and only the third group has terminal flowers, i.e. three fourths of the plants should have axial flowers and one fourth should have terminal flowers. Mendel got an experimental ratio of 3.14 to 1, very close to the mathematical expectations.

Apart from flower position, Mendel used six other pairs of alternative traits in his experiments (including round and wrinkled seeds, long and short stems and green and yellow peas). He found that all behaved in the same manner, i.e. gave a 3 to 1 ratio of dominant to recessive traits in the F2 generation. Each of the ratios differed slightly from 3 to 1, but not enough to raise any serious doubts. Mendel studied large numbers of F2 plants, which was very important. Had he used smaller numbers the results might have deviated more from the mathematical expectation. Such results would be difficult to analyse and interpret. In his experiments, across all seven pairs of traits, Mendel observed 14,889 dominant traits and 5,010 recessive traits in the F2 generation—a ratio of 2.98 to 1, which is as close to a 3 to 1 ratio as you could hope to achieve under experimental conditions where chance assortment is involved.

The modern term for Mendel's factors is genes. Mendel's interpretation for what happens in such a cross is accepted today as the correct analysis not only for plants, but also for animals. Mendel's system of nomenclature was to represent dominant genetic factors using a capital letter for the dominant gene and the same letter in the lower case for the recessive alternative. The letter is the first letter in the trait which is less common. For flower position, T means axial and t means terminal. That nomenclature is still in use today, e.g. h for the haemophilia gene (bleeder's disease) and H for the alternative dominant gene that is associated with normal blood-clotting.

Of course, it has been known from time immemorial that characteristics are inherited from generation to generation, but until Mendel's brilliant work, nobody understood the mechanism of inheritance. Mendel's identification of the fundamental factors that determine an organism's characteristics and how these factors, which we now call genes, can independently sort and segregate from generation to generation was a revolutionary breakthrough.

Mendel reported his results at a meeting of the Association for Natural Research in Brno in 1865 and published the work that same year in a book under the title *Treatises on Plant Hybrids*. The work was ahead of its time and was not appreciated by the wider scientific community (nor indeed was it widely read). In 1900 there was a famous rediscovery and appreciation of Mendel's work by Carl Correns in Germany, Hugo de Vries in Holland and Erich von Tschermak-Seysenegg in Austria.

Mendel's work laid the firm foundation for the modern science of genetics. The rise of molecular biology this century identified the chemical nature of the gene as DNA and demonstrated how the gene determines characteristics—by controlling and specifying what proteins are synthesised. We are now in the middle of a spectacular explosion of genetic based developments, including screening for genetic disease, genetic therapy for disease, genetic engineering of organisms to produce various useful products and cloning of organisms.

In 1936, the British mathematician R. A. Fischer analysed Mendel's results and came to the conclusion that they were simply too good to be true! Fischer claimed that the principles of variation statistics would prevent Mendel from achieving experimental segregation ratios so close to the perfect 3 to 1 ratio. In other words, Mendel, or his assistants, had 'touched up' their data to make it conform to theoretical predictions. Much subsequent work, however, has failed to support Fisher's doubts. Mendel's experiments stand up. He achieved almost perfect results because he was simply that good. Pure genius.

Mendel was disheartened by the lack of response to his published work. He was elected as Abbot of the monastery in 1868. The heavy workload of running the monastery took him away from his beloved experiments. Shortly before his death in 1883 he said: 'My scientific studies have afforded me great gratification, and I am convinced it will not be long before the whole world acknowledges the results of my work'. Seventeen years later his prediction came true.

Deciphering the Structure of the Hereditary Material

People have wondered since ancient times how the characteristics of parents are passed on to children. The puzzle was finally solved in detail in the 1950s in probably the greatest scientific advance of the twentieth century. This breakthrough gave birth to genetic engineering, molecular genetics and modern biotechnology. These developments touch all our lives—and we are only at the beginning. Mere mention of the terms DNA and the genetic code conjures up images of Francis Crick and James Watson, who solved the structure of DNA in 1953. But, as is the nature of science, their breakthrough was only possible because of previous discoveries made by many other scientists.

In the fourth century BC Aristotle proposed that semen contains plans that direct the unformed maternal blood to shape offspring. In the Middle Ages, Thomas Aquinas 'explained' that vigorous seed develops into males and weak seed produces females. Later, sperm cells were examined under the light microscope. It was 'observed' that each contains a tiny pre-formed child, termed the *homunculus*. The mother was considered to merely incubate the homunculus, who emerged as a baby nine months later.

Modern genetics began with Gregor Mendel's brilliant experiments on heritability in pea plants. Mendel showed that discrete hereditary elements (genes) are responsible for hereditary traits. These genes are passed on by both parents and the genes can independently sort and segregate between offspring (see the previous chapter on the work of Gregor Mendel).

The scientific world was not ready for Mendel's results, published in 1865. His concept of the sorting and segregation of discrete hereditary units could not be accommodated by the crude understanding of the cell then available. He also used a statistical approach which was foreign to the current biological thinking.

Mendel's work was rediscovered at the turn of the century, by which time the rest of science was 'up to speed'. In the meantime chromosomes (the structures in the cell nucleus that contain the hereditary material) had been discovered. Mitosis—the process whereby chromosomes duplicate and are shared equally between two daughter cells when the parent cell divides—was understood, as was meiosis. Meiosis is the process whereby a parent cell divides twice to produce four sex cells (egg or sperm). The chromosomes duplicate only once during meoisis and consequently each germ cell receives half the chromosome number of the parent. Chromosome number is restored when a sperm combines with (fertilises) an egg to form an embryo. Mendel's theory could now be projected onto structures visible in the microscope. Also, by now the use of statistics was common in biology.

An explosion of developments in genetics began. It became clear that genes are arranged linearly along chromosomes and that they can undergo sudden permanent changes (mutation) resulting in changed traits in the organism. Genetics could also explain the mechanism of evolution. Mutations are the main source of novelty in evolution and natural selection chooses organisms bearing novel genes that make them better suited to survive in the environment.

Genetic understanding made it possible to design breeding programmes to improve animal and plant varieties and in medicine it opened the way to design interventions for the prevention and cure of disease.

But the molecular mechanism whereby the gene exerts its effect remained a mystery. However, interesting speculation was in the air. In 1945, Erwin Schrödinger published a book *What is Life?* He suggested that the gene is a one dimensional aperiodic crystal of a few repeating elements whose pattern of succession represents the hereditary information.

In 1944 O. T. Avery and co-workers showed that genes must be embodied in deoxyribonucleic acid (DNA), known since 1920 to be a major component of chromosomes. However, structurally it was thought that DNA was made of identical repeat units and therefore incapable of bearing information.

In 1952, A. D. Herschey and M. Chase again demonstrated that genes are made of DNA. By now much more was known about the structure of DNA. In 1950 Edwin Chargaff had shown that DNA from different biological sources showed distinct differences and could carry information.

Four kinds of chemical structures are linked together in DNA. These are deoxyribose, phosphoric acid, purine bases (adenine—A and guanine—G) and pyrimidine bases (thymine—T and cytosine—C). Chargaff showed that DNA from different sources had different relative amounts of A, T, G and C and that, regardless of source, A and T were always present in equal proportions and G and C were always present in equal proportions.

In the late 1940s and early 1950s, W. T. Astbury, Maurice Wilkins and Rosalind Franklin produced vital X-ray diffraction pictures of DNA showing it was probably a two stranded helical structure. Francis Crick and James Watson, using X-ray diffraction and models, and drawing on all the available evidence, solved the structure of DNA in 1953.

The DNA molecule is a double helix in which two strands wind around each other. A repeating combination of sugar and phosphoric acid (deoxyribose-phosphate) makes up the backbone of each strand and the bases protrude from these backbones into the heart of the double helix. A (adenine) always pairs with T on the other strand, and G always pairs with C. Information in DNA resides in the base sequences. One unit of information is represented by a sequence of three bases. The four letters of the genetic alphabet (A, T, G, C) can therefore form sixty-four 'words' or units of information (4 x 4 x 4).

The structure of the genetic material is, like all great truths, elegantly simple and simply beautiful. Watson and Crick made their breakthrough as young men. They have since been fêted as heroes. And indeed they are great scientists. But they enjoy their fame because science was ready to hear what they had to say. Their results were not premature, like those of poor Gregor Mendel, who died a lonely death with his great work unappreciated.

The Potential of Genetic Engineering

Genetic engineering, in broad terms, means the deliberate manipulation of genetic material. Specifically, it usually means taking defined bits of genetic material from one organism and inserting them into another organism. The potential of genetic engineering is vast and varied. It offers great hope for the efficient detection and treatment of disease, for the improvement of agriculture and even for the control of pollution. As with the introduction of any new powerful technology there are worries and dangers attending. (Many of the questions raised are about ethical issues and I will deal with these questions in the next chapter.)

The basic unit of organisation in all biological organisms is the cell. Every cell contains genetic material which controls its day-to-day activity and, when the cell divides in two to form daughter cells, exact copies of the genetic material are passed to both offspring. The genetic material contains the information that bears on every aspect of the cell's activity. The genetic material is composed of the chemical DNA, a very long molecule made up of units called nucleotides. There are four different nucleotides and the information content of the DNA is carried in the nucleotide sequence. This information determines the types of proteins that are synthesised in the cell and these proteins carry out the cell's activity. The length of DNA information that codes for one protein is called a gene. An alteration in a gene will result in the production of an altered protein, which usually has serious negative consequences for the cell. The introduction of a new gene into a cell gives the cell the capacity to make a new protein.

Medicine lists over three thousand human genetic diseases—that is, diseases resulting from alterations in genetic material and inherited from one generation to the next. These diseases contribute considerably to the burden of human misery. Typical examples are cystic fibrosis, muscular dystrophy and haemophilia. Cystic fibrosis is the most common inherited fatal disease of Caucasians, with a frequency of about one in two thousand births. The genetic defect results in the absence of a protein whose function is to regulate certain aspects of salt balance. This causes the mucus-lining on the outside of cells to become thick and turgid resulting in obstruction of the pancreas and chronic infection of the lungs, which are the usual cause of death in childhood or early adulthood.

For many years molecular biologists (biologists who work at the molecular level) have been making intensive efforts to identify and characterise the altered genes that cause the major genetic diseases. These efforts have been rewarded with considerable success, for example in cystic fibrosis and muscular dystrophy. Characterisation of the gene allows two possibilities—genetic testing and genetic therapy. Genetic testing means using a probe that recognises a gene in order to see if a subject is carrying the altered gene. Genetic testing could be carried out on a widespread basis (screening) using tissue samples that are easily obtainable, such as blood samples. Genetic testing can also be done on embryos in the earliest stages of development. Such tests also identify the sex of the embryo.

Intensive and very promising efforts are now underway to develop effective techniques for gene therapy of cystic fibrosis and muscular dystrophy. Gene therapy means compensating for a genetic defect by introducing good copies of the gene into the cells of the subject who is naturally producing defective copies.

There is enormous potential for genetic engineering in agriculture in the development of new and improved strains of plants and animals. The general principle involved is not new to agriculturalists. For centuries, animal and plant breeders have used the laws of inheritance to deliberately and gradually modify species in order to enhance agricultural production. Left to her own devices, Nature would never have produced a cow that yields ten gallons of milk per day!

Natural breeding methods are slow and gradual. If a breeder wants to introduce a new desirable characteristic into a species, he or she must breed that species with a closely related species containing the desired characteristic. The offspring will show the desired characteristic, but also other unwanted characteristics that have been imported from the second species. Several additional cycles of breeding must now be planned in order to gradually get rid of the undesired characteristics, while retaining the valuable characteristic.

The procedures of genetic engineering are much quicker and more flexible. One is not restricted to interbreeding closely related species—genes from one species can be introduced into another species that is not related to the first. Also the technique allows the precise introduction of specific genes only and there is no accompanying range of other unwanted characteristics that have to be subsequently and slowly bred out over many generations.

Using genetic engineering techniques it will also be possible to develop crops that thrive under inhospitable conditions or are particularly disease-resistant. The first genetically engineered food to go on sale in the USA was a tomato that had been genetically altered so that it did not become soft and mushy as it ripened. It will be possible in the future to genetically engineer meat animals that grow much faster than conventional strains and that yield higher quality meat. There are presently many examples where bacteria are altered by genetic engineering and used for large-scale production of an important protein that is expensive and difficult to produce in quantity by conventional methods, for example proteins of medical importance such as insulin.

Genetic engineering has produced several examples of transgenic animals—animals into which a gene from another species has been introduced. For example, sheep have been produced bearing a human gene that produces a protein which is secreted into the milk—a blood-clotting factor that is needed by people with haemophilia. Several transgenic animals have been patented by the companies that produced them. These developments raise the prospect of a new agricultural revolution of transgenic farm animals that make valuable human proteins needed to treat disease.

Ethical Issues Raised by Genetic Manipulation

In the previous chapter I gave an overview of the huge potential of genetic manipulation, principally in the fields of medicine and agriculture. Genetic testing can identify carriers of genetic disease and genetic therapy has the potential to cure genetic disease. Genetic engineering can produce new strains of plants and animals to enhance agricultural production. Scientific and technical progress in these areas has been rapid. However, the technical capacity to achieve something is an entirely separate matter from considerations as to whether or not the procedure is permissible on ethical ground. The development of genetic manipulation techniques has raised many questions that remain topics of hot debate.

It would be easy to carry out genetic testing on a widespread screening basis. There are dangers involved here. Should the identity of the carrier of a genetic disease be identified to anyone except the carrier and, in many such cases, is it even desirable that the carrier knows? For example, suppose you have a genetic nerve disease which displays no symptoms until you reach your forties. Then, progressive loss of mental functioning sets in, followed by death in ten years. If you are informed you have this disease while still young, what effect will it have on your quality of life? On the other hand, how can you make an informed decision about whether or not to have children if you are not aware of your condition?

Insurance companies already seek information about family history of conditions with a hereditary component, such as heart disease, and use this information when assessing premium levels. If these companies had access to widespread genetic screening data they would have an unprecedented ability to forecast morbidity and life expectancy. In such cases some people might be unable to obtain any insurance at all. Similar considerations apply to employment prospects for such individuals if genetic screening data were made available to employers.

Then there's the whole question of genetic testing to provide information about potential offspring. On one level this could simply involve genetic counselling. This occurs where a known carrier of a genetic disease gets professional advice on the probability that a potential offspring would inherit the genetic defect and, in that event, what the outlook for the child would be. Based on the advice given, the subject decides whether or not the risks merit going ahead and having a child. To avail of genetic counselling in this manner would be seen as sensible and decent by the vast majority of people.

However, it is now possible to do genetic testing on embryos in the very earliest stages of development. At this stage it is also possible to tell the sex of the developing embryo. Making decisions based on genetic testing of embryos is a highly controversial area. For example, many people would feel that it is reasonable to terminate pregnancy if genetic testing of the embryo shows a defect which makes it certain that the born child would lead a miserable life ending in early death. Many other people would vehemently protest that any artificial termination is absolutely prohibited on moral grounds, despite the undoubted accuracy of the medical prognosis.

And what about terminating matters if the embryo is of the 'wrong' sex? While this might seem to be a fundamentally inhuman act, there are parts of the world where it is common because of the strong social preference for boys over girls. Indeed, such preferences are not unknown in our own culture. All of which prompts the question—should genetic testing of embryos be allowed except under the most tightly circumscribed circumstances?

When considering gene therapy one must distinguish between therapeutic and non-therapeutic intervention. Gene therapy to cure a disease is therapeutic; gene therapy to improve intelligence (this is presently not possible) or some other characteristic, e.g. height, is non-therapeutic. A procedure might be considered ethical when undertaken for therapeutic purposes and unethical when undertaken for non-therapeutic purposes. For example, choosing the sex of a child, for reasons of social pressures, might be considered unethical, whereas deciding not to have boy children because of an inherited fatal genetic defect, expressed only in males, could be considered an ethical decision.

A distinction must also be drawn between genetic manipulation of germ cells and somatic cells. Germ cells (sperm in males and eggs in females) are those involved in procreation and inheritance. Somatic cells are the ordinary body tissue cells (muscle, nerve etc). Genetic changes made to a person's somatic cells end with the death of that individual. Genetic changes in a germ cell can be passed on to future generations. If mistakes were made in the genetic engineering of germ cells, these mistakes could spread through the population in future generations. Therefore, genetic engineering of germ cells is banned in humans.

Less scrupulous considerations apply where animals are concerned. There are many examples of transgenic animals, where a gene from one species is introduced into another species in order to facilitate the production of some useful protein product. Animals have also been genetically manipulated to express diseases similar to human conditions. The justification here is to facilitate widespread study of the disease and in ways that are not possible with human subjects. An oncomouse has been genetically engineered in America and attempts have been made to patent it. This mouse develops cancer within several months of birth. Whatever about producing healthy transgenic animals to make useful protein products, one must have grave reservations about deliberately engineering sick animals.

People are wary about the whole concept of genetic manipulation. This is understandable because what we are talking about is a fundamental manipulation of life. An analogy can be drawn with the developments in nuclear physics earlier this century. Learning the secrets of the atomic nucleus gave physicists the power to manipulate matter in ways that hitherto had been impossible. Some of the possible manipulations of the atom, stemming from discoveries earlier this century, are good for humanity and some are not. On the positive side I will list nuclear power (at least the intention was good) and the production of special forms of radioactive elements that are very useful in medicine and scientific research. On the negative side we had the nightmarish development of nuclear weapons. Similarly the new genetic techniques allow us to manipulate living organisms in ways that were hitherto not possible. We must strive to use this power only for good ends. This will require considerable wisdom and considerable courage.

Sexual and Asexual Reproduction and Clones

When the news broke about Dolly, the cloned sheep, I thought of the summer's day when I called to see my mother. I found her cloning plants in the back garden. Had I been wearing my Superman spectacles, that allow me to see incredibly tiny things, I would have seen that the whole garden was a hive of cloning activity. Bacteria were cloning themselves all over the place. I would have seen aphids busily cloning themselves by the hedge and, down in the far corner, the bees and the wasps were also at it. Cloning is 'old hat' to Mother Nature.

Biological organisms reproduce themselves either by sexual or asexual methods, and some organisms can employ both methods. In asexual reproduction, the new individual (offspring) is produced by a single parent and derives genetic material from that single parent only. In sexual reproduction the new individual has two parents and usually derives half its genetic complement from one parent and half from the other parent. The recent cloning of the sheep Dolly, in Scotland, is a special example of artificially contrived reproduction, where all the genetic content of the offspring comes from its single and only parent.

The genetic content of an organism resides in its chromosomes. A biological clone is defined as an individual that is genetically identical to its single parent. For example, when simple single-celled organisms wish to reproduce they do so by dividing in two. The chromosomes of the 'parent' cell duplicate prior to the cell dividing, and each daughter cell receives an identical copy of the parent's chromosomes. Both daughters are genetically identical to the parent and are therefore clones of the original.

The asexual production of clones is also common in horticulture. The type of cloning my mother was doing simply involves sticking twigs ('cuttings'), cut from plants she fancied when out for a stroll, into the ground. The cutting takes root and grows into a new plant identical to the plant of which it was once but a twig.

Asexual reproduction can also take place in multicellular animals. The more primitive the animal, the more likely it is to be capable of asexual reproduction. For example, you could cut a sponge or a flatworm into small parts and each part, if kept in its usual environment, would grow into a complete organism. These new organisms can be considered to be clones of the original.

Many insects, including bees, wasps and aphids, also commonly produce clones of themselves. Technically this is classified as a form of sexual reproduction, because a sex cell, the egg, is involved. However, the process differs radically from the usual form of sexual reproduction seen in higher animals.

This special process in insects is called parthenogenesis. In aphids, an unfertilised egg cell containing only a half set of chromosomes develops into an embryo, and subsequently into an adult insect, without the assistance of any sperm cell. The egg's half set of chromosomes duplicates itself to produce a full set, the egg divides and continues to divide to become a fully developed organism. All of the chromosomes in the new organism come from the female parent. Again we are dealing with a form of cloning.

I once heard a well-known Irish feminist declare at a public meeting: 'we (women) don't need men; we can have children by parthenogenesis'. She may have been joking, but she sounded serious. If she was serious, she could scarcely have made a nastier statement.

Could a woman conceive by parthenogenesis? I don't know the answer to this question. In most forms of life an egg requires activation by a sperm in order to start dividing and to develop into an embryo. However, in several cases it has been shown that it is possible to spark this activation experimentally and to obtain parthenogenetic reproduction. For example, sea-urchin eggs can be stimulated to divide by placing them in strong salt water. Frog eggs have been stimulated similarly by pricking them with needles. There is a report that rabbit eggs were also successfully stimulated in this manner. A certain breed of white turkey produces eggs (unfertilised) that sometimes develop into embryos when incubated. Some of these embryos eventually hatch and go on to produce adults—turkeys without fathers.

Conventional sexual reproduction is the norm for human beings and for most organisms that are at our general level of complexity. Sexual reproduction is effected by the union of a sperm cell from the father with an egg cell from the mother. The new individual receives an equal amount of genetic material from each parent.

The genetic material—genes—resides on the chromosomes, located in the nucleus of the cell. Our bodies are composed of cells of two types—somatic cells and germ cells. The somatic cells make up our tissues, such as muscle, kidneys, liver, etc. The germ cells are involved in procreation—sperm cells in the male and egg cells in the female. Somatic cells contain twenty-three pairs of chromosomes, one set coming originally from the father and the other set from the mother. Somatic cells increase in numbers by each dividing into two and, in this way, tissues grow and maintain themselves. Prior to somatic cell division (mitosis) the chromosomes duplicate themselves and each daughter cell receives the full complement of twenty-three pairs of chromosomes. On the other hand, when germ cells are formed, each cell receives not twenty-three pairs, but twenty-three individual chromosomes. Union of the sperm with the egg restores the somatic situation of twenty-three pairs of chromosomes in the fertilised egg. The subsequent development into an adult consisting of billions of cells is effected by countless cell divisions beginning with the first division of the fertilised egg cell. Each somatic cell in the body contains the same twenty-three pairs of chromosomes which constitute the entire genetic blueprint of the organism.

Cells of different tissues in the body look different from each other and perform different tasks, even though every cell contains identical genetic information. The explanation is that these differentiated cells use only part of the entire genetic blueprint information. Parts of the blueprint not in use in a particular tissue are switched off.

Since an ordinary somatic cell has identical genetic information to that in the original fertilised egg, biologists have long wondered if it is possible to trigger a somatic cell to develop into a whole new organism—into a clone of the parent cell. Many attempts have been made over the years to achieve such cloning, and with some success.

The phenomenon of parthenogenesis shows that the environment within the egg can trigger a programme of development in the chromosomes that results in the eventual formation of an adult organism. In attempting to clone an organism from a differentiated somatic cell, the approach has been to extract the nucleus from such a cell, remove the nucleus from an egg cell and replace it with the nucleus from the differentiated somatic cell—and hope that the egg cell environment would trigger the developmental programme. Success has been achieved in this manner in cloning tadpoles. However, not until Dolly was there ever a success in triggering the chromosomes from a somatic cell from an adult mammal into a full developmental programme. Dolly was cloned from an udder cell taken from an adult sheep.

I will return to the subject of cloning in the next chapter to discuss human cloning.

Cloning Human Beings

It didn't take long. The ink was scarcely dry on the report of the cloning of Dolly the sheep before the American physicist, Dr Richard Seed, declared that he wanted to clone human beings within two years. He believes that 'this will be the first serious step in becoming one with God'. Seed's proposal is outrageous. The debate on the ethics of human cloning has scarcely begun. Even if human cloning was ethically acceptable, it would be wildly premature at this stage from a technical point of view. In any event, human cloning would offend against the sound biological sense of sexual reproduction.

Two organisms are defined as clones of each other if they are genetically identical. Cloning occurs commonly in nature by an asexual process. When an amoeba wishes to reproduce, it simply duplicates its genetic material and divides into two daughter cells, each of which receives an identical copy of the parent's genes. The daughters are clones of the parent. Mammals, on the other hand, produce offspring by sexual means.

Mammals contain body (somatic) cells (liver, muscle, etc.) and sex cells— sperm in men, eggs in women. Every somatic cell contains a double set of genes, one from the father and one from the mother. The sex cell contains only a single set of genes, some from the father, some from the mother. When a sperm fertilises an egg, the somatic cells of the offspring again contain full sets of genes from both parents. Sex fulfils several important biological functions. For example, it generates variety by combining characteristics of different people.

In the everyday wear and tear of the life of a cell, the genetic material suffers an inevitable level of background damage. Because genes are so important, they must be repaired when they become damaged. If the damage is not repaired it must be masked. Sexual reproduction plays a vital role in this process of genetic hygiene. During the sexual process, repairs are made to damaged genetic material. Also, existing damage (mutation) that has evaded the repair machinery can usually be masked. The offspring contains a full set of genes for all characteristics from both parents. Let us say the mother of a child has a defective gene for characteristic X. The likelihood is that the father's gene for X is good. The child will therefore have one good gene for X, which is usually sufficient to produce a normal X characteristic. Sex between brother and sister is taboo because of the greatly increased likelihood that both will have damaged genes for the same characteristics, masked in each but coming together in the offspring to produce a sick child.

None of the genetic advantages of sex apply to reproduction by cloning. Cloning would be the ultimate incestuous relationship whereby, in effect, you would marry yourself. It should never be introduced as a widespread option for human reproduction.

Dr Seed proposes to use the Dolly technique to clone human beings. Briefly, Dolly was cloned as follows. A cell was taken from the adult Dolly's udder and its nucleus (containing the hereditary material) was removed. An egg cell was taken from a second sheep and its nucleus was replaced by Dolly's nucleus. This egg cell, bearing Dolly's genes, was implanted in the womb of a third sheep, who produced the famous lamb in due course.

But the above story is incomplete. It describes the case that worked, not the many that failed. Many nuclei were inserted into many egg cells to produce embryos that were implanted into ewes. There was a high rate of miscarriage—two hundred and twenty-seven transferred adult nuclei were tried to produce one healthy lamb.

It is, therefore, from a technical point of view alone, far too early to carry out human cloning. The high failure rate would be unacceptable in a human context. Also, before cloning could be seriously contemplated for humans, extensive work would need to be done on a species that is much closer to humans than sheep, such as the chimpanzee.

Although the cloning of Dolly was a landmark achievement in the history of biology, we do not yet know how successful the process is. In the meantime Dolly the clone successfully mated in the normal manner with a ram and gave birth in the normal manner to her own lamb Bonnie. However we must still wait to see if Dolly will live out a normal lifespan in a normal manner. She was 'born' of adult somatic DNA that bore the normal 'wear and tear' characteristic of such materials. Analysis of Dolly's DNA has recently shown that in terms of 'wear and tear', it is several years older than Dolly's chronological age.

But the whole idea of cloning human beings now is outrageous anyway because ethical norms have not been established in this area. It is not at all clear whether cloning of human beings will ever be ethically permissible, under any circumstances. Presently, public opinion is completely opposed to the idea. If a maverick scientist produced a human clone there would be a massive public outcry. Science as a whole would be blamed for 'sinning against nature' and politicians would be forced to introduce draconian controls on all sorts of scientific research.

Dr Seed wants to clone human beings in order to help infertile people. Of course infertile people should be helped, and a variety of widely acceptable means are already available, ranging from adoption to in-vitro fertilisation techniques. To suggest that the problem of infertility is so desperately urgent that we must rush headlong at human cloning before we are ethically and technically ready, or rationally convinced, is ridiculous.

In the USA, President Clinton has instituted a five-year moratorium on research into human cloning in federal funded programmes and has asked for a similar moratorium on a voluntary basis in non-federal agencies. Dr Seed is prepared to move to another state in order to carry out his plan. It is to be hoped that Dr Seed's scientific colleagues will be able to persuade him to desist. If not, more effective methods will have to be employed.

Note: See postscript at the end of the next chapter.

The Ethics of Human Cloning

The successful cloning of Dolly the sheep was announced to an unsuspecting world in February 1997. Since then there have been rapid developments in the field of cloning adult mammals. For example, mice have been successfully cloned at the University of Hawaii, and in that laboratory, the process has been extended to produce clones of clones, and clones of clones of clones. Also, the famous Dolly is proving so far to be a normal animal. She was mated with a ram and subsequently gave birth to her own lamb. Those rapid developments prompt me to return to the subject of human cloning and specifically to ethical questions raised by the prospect.

We could have been debating the ethics of cloning for the past thrity years, but we weren't. While Dolly is a very recent development, the experimental production of animal clones is not. In the late 1960s J. B. Gurdon cloned tadpole cells, which grew into adult frogs. In my opinion, no great insight was necessary at that stage to conclude that this type of technology would soon be successful with adult mammals. Dolly was born in February 1997, the first clone to be made of an adult mammal. Since then the world has been in a tizzy of fearful anticipation of possible consequences.

As I pointed out in the previous chapter, it would be wildly premature from a technical point of view, leaving considerations of ethics aside altogether, to go ahead now with the cloning of human adults. This consideration alone is more than sufficient reason to ban human cloning for the present. We don't know yet if clones of adult sheep have a normal lifespan, have normal good health or behave over their lifespan in a normal manner. But let us assume that the animal clones will prove to be normal in all respects, and that improvements in the technique and its successful application in primate cousins of man will make it virtually certain that the technique could be used successfully to clone adult humans. Will it then be ethical, under any circumstances, to produce human clones?

Human cloning has been seriously proposed as an option for providing children for childless couples. Some experts have claimed that the ethical guidelines that apply to in-vitro fertilisation should also apply to cloning. In this view cloning is just another technique, equivalent to in-vitro fertilisation, to allow people, who cannot procreate in the usual manner, to have children. But this opinion is surely mistaken. The child produced by in-vitro fertilisation has a biological father and a biological mother and, although fertilisation of the egg by the sperm and subsequent implantation is achieved only with much technical assistance, the resulting child is a product of the same basic biological procedure that has produced every human child ever born on earth.

The first deliberately engineered human clone will mark a qualitative change. While it is true that sometimes a fertilised egg divides in two to produce identical twins that are genetic clones of each other, the fertilised egg that divides in two is produced by the normal sexual mechanism and is a genetic mixture of two parents. An artificially produced human clone would be a genetic copy of its lone parent. Such a revolutionary process surely calls for its own ethical guidelines, not hand-me-down guidelines designed to deal with an altogether different process.

I think it is broadly accepted that, as a civilised norm, children should be conceived out of love and reared as autonomous individuals. Such an ethical norm rules out the specific case of producing clones who must live in some predetermined way. For example, it would be unethical to produce a clone for the purpose of supplying a desperately needed body organ for a close genetic relative. It would be unethical to clone a person who is hugely talented in some field in order to reproduce that talent.

But what about the case of a childless couple who are desperately longing for a child and for whom, for some reason, in-vitro fertilisation will not work? Would cloning be ethically permissible here under circumstances where there is no doubt that the couple would love the child and rear him or her as an autonomous individual? It seems to me that this question entirely hinges on what weight we put on the 'right' to have a child who is closely genetically related to us.

I have no doubt that the pain of childlessness is felt intensely by some people. Nevertheless, I don't think that this problem is sufficiently big to merit being solved by the introduction of human cloning. In a world where so many children are starved, neglected and abused, it would seem to be grossly out of proportion to take such a huge step as the introduction of cloning in order to provide children for a small number of childless couples. It is also hard to understand how any medical doctor can advocate human cloning in order to give a childless couple an intensely longed-for baby, while, in the clinic around the corner, perfectly normal human foetuses are routinely aborted.

It seems to me that if human cloning is ever to be allowed it should only be as a last resort to solve some extraordinarily important problem. Adoption has brought great joy and comfort to countless couples and the techniques of in-vitro fertilisation are under constant development. These two options would seem to be sufficient to deal with the problem of providing children for childless couples for the foreseeable future.

Modern genetic science has raised a wide range of issues. The introduction of practical and ethical guidelines to regulate many of these issues, e.g. genetic modification of plants and animals, is seen by many to be more urgent than dealing with the possibility of human cloning, because many of these practices are already with us. But, since Dr Seed, the American physicist who wants to produce a human clone within two years, has declared his mind, can human cloning be far away? Certainly not if we do not vigorously debate the matter.

Postscript: In June 1999, shortly before the publication of this book, it was announced that the world's first human clone had been made by an American biotechnology company. A cell from a research scientist was combined with a cow's egg from which the genes had already been removed. The clone–egg divided up to the thirty-two cell stage before it was destroyed. Of course, we don't know if this clone would have developed into a viable baby if the process had been allowed to continue, but the initial development seemed to be progressing smoothly.

The Nature and Power of Genetic Fingerprinting

Each of us has a pattern of information in our genetic make-up that is unique. The only exceptions to this are identical twins, each of whom has an identical genetic make-up. Just as fingerprints can be used to identify an individual, so can patterns in our genetic make-up, and with even greater accuracy. The genetic technique, known as genetic fingerprinting, is now in widespread use and frequently hits the headlines because of its applications in forensic science. Genetic fingerprinting is a far more powerful technique than classical fingerprinting because it can be used not only to identify a person, but it can also identify to whom that person is genetically related.

Our bodies are composed of trillions of fundamental units called cells. Each body (somatic) cell contains a complete copy of the individual's genetic make-up. The genetic material is organised into long threads called chromosomes. Humans have twenty-three pairs of chromosomes in each body cell. One member of each pair comes from the father and the other comes from the mother. The genetic material within each chromosome is DNA which is also a long string. There are two strands in each DNA string. The two strands wind about each other in double helical fashion. Each strand is composed of successive units called nucleotides. There are only four kinds of nucleotides in DNA and they are denoted by the letters A, T, G and C. These are the letters of the genetic code alphabet.

The linear sequence of the genetic alphabet, in groups of three, specifies the genetic information. The two strands of DNA are linked together by loose bonds that form between the letters that make up each individual strand. The inter-letter bonding is very specific—A always binds to T and G always binds to C. Thus, the two strands of a DNA string have complementary sequences of nucleotide letters dictated by this bonding

The use of genetic fingerprinting to establish the identity of a parent

rule. For example the sequence A G T C on one strand would be bonded to the complementary sequence T C A G on the other strand. The most important information coded in the DNA is divided up into segments called genes. Each gene contains the information necessary to manufacture a specific protein in the cell. Apart from DNA, proteins are the most important chemicals in a cell and carry out most of the cell's activity.

In addition to genes, chromosomal DNA also carries special regions of nucleotide repeat base sequences called minisatellites. These do not carry information codes for the manufacture of proteins. The number of locations of minisatellite regions is unique to the DNA of every particular individual. Half of this unique pattern is contributed by the father and half by the mother. The detection and identification of this minisatellite DNA pattern is the basis for genetic fingerprinting. The location of the minisatellite regions in DNA is detected using special probes (segments of DNA having complementary base sequences to the minisatellite regions) followed by selective staining and visualisation of the bound probe. The probes are not used against intact DNA molecules but against molecules that have been broken down into smaller pieces. This breaking of the DNA is not a random process but is carried out in a very specific fashion by the use of special enzymes (catalysts) called restriction enzymes that break DNA only at certain nucleotide sequences.

The full procedure for carrying out DNA fingerprinting on an individual would go as follows. First of all, a small sample of cells is taken and the DNA is isolated from them. The DNA is then fragmented using the restriction enzyme and the various bits of DNA are separated out from each other according to size on a special gel (a thin sheet of jelly-like consistency). The bits of DNA separate out from each other in the gel, stacked one over the other in size sequence, from the largest bits at the top of the gel to the smallest at the bottom. The gel is now reacted with the minisatellite probe, which binds to the gel wherever it finds a complementary target. A special staining procedure is now employed to stain the gel everywhere the probe has reacted. The end product, the 'genetic fingerprint', is the stained gel. It is a sequence of darker and lighter horizontal bands, stacked one over the other from the top to the bottom of the gel. It looks quite similar to the bar code that is now printed on all product packaging. Just like the bar code, the genetic fingerprint uniquely identifies the subject from whom it was taken. About half the bands in an individuals genetic fingerprint have been inherited from the mother and the other half from the father.

The technique of genetic fingerprinting frequently hits the headlines in cases where it is used to establish the identify of a child's parent or to establish the identify of the perpetrator of some crime. Take the following hypothetical case. A woman gives birth to a baby. The father must be one of two men, but she cannot be sure which is the actual father. The matter can be readily decided by comparing the genetic fingerprints of the baby, the mother and the two potential fathers.

Very small samples of human tissue will suffice to allow a genetic fingerprint to be made, for example a few drops of blood, several hairs, some skin scrapings. This is very useful in forensic science when small biological samples, collected from the scene of the crime, can be used to conclusively implicate or rule out a suspect. Genetic fingerprinting is a very powerful technique in incriminating or exonerating alleged rapists. A vaginal swab taken soon after the perpetration of a rape will contain samples of the victim's cells and also of the rapist's semen. When a genetic fingerprint of the victim's DNA is compared to a genetic fingerprint recovered from the swab, the bands corresponding to the rapist's semen can be easily identified.

These bands can then be used to incriminate or exonerate suspects in rape cases by comparing them to genetic fingerprints prepared from suspects' semen samples.

One interesting and very useful application of genetic fingerprinting is the identification of children who 'disappeared' in Argentina during the military rule from 1976 to 1983 and their reunification with their relatives. A genetic data bank of blood samples from relatives of children who went missing has been established and is used to check out the identities of people, now adults, suspected or known to have gone missing under the military regime.

Medicine and Disease

Why is Human Life Expectancy Greater Now than in the Past?

Average western life expectancy in the year 1900 was forty-nine years—the figure today is slightly better than seventy-five years. The average life expectancy now in Ireland is seventy-six years. It is widely assumed that this impressive improvement has been effected by modern medicine, improved standards of nutrition and good hygiene practices. Amongst these three factors, pride of place is given to modern medicine. However, there is evidence to indicate that neither modern medicine, nutrition nor hygiene have played such leading roles in improving life expectancy. The American epidemiologist, Leonard Sagan (author of *The Health of Nations*, Basic Books, 1987), and others argue that our improved health and longevity is mainly due to psychological factors that have developed and strengthened over the past one hundred and fifty years.

Sagan quotes lifespan statistics amongst different social classes in Britain. Prior to the introduction of the National Health Service in 1946, the lowest socioeconomic groups had long experienced much worse life expectancy than the most affluent groups. This was assumed to be caused by economic barriers preventing poorer people from having access to medical care. However, today, more than fifty years later, the relative disparity in life expectancy between the most affluent and the least affluent groups in Britain remains, despite open access by all to full medical care.

The introduction of antibiotics into clinical medicine during the 1940s is generally reckoned to mark the turning point in humankind's fight against infectious diseases. Clearly diseases such as tuberculosis and typhoid no longer claim lives at the rate they did in the past. However, death rates from these diseases had been declining in

Scandinavia and the English-speaking countries since the middle of the nineteenth century, long before antibiotics were available. By the time the first antibiotics were introduced the death rates had dwindled to a fraction of what they once had been.

Nevertheless, antibiotics were spectacularly effective for a time after their introduction. However, their effectiveness has now been seriously compromised due to widespread overprescription by the medical profession. Antibiotics are frequently administered to treat colds and influenza despite the fact that there is no evidence that they have any primary effectiveness in such cases. Overprescription of antibiotics allows the bacteria against which these drugs are active to gradually develop resistance against them.

Immunisation is also widely believed to enhance life expectancy. There is no doubt that vaccines against infectious diseases such as polio, whooping cough and diphtheria do protect people from these diseases and so save lives and spare many from permanent disabilities. However, there is little evidence that immunisation has caused a significant decline in overall mortality rates. Deaths from whooping cough, measles and diphtheria, for example, were already under control by the end of the Second World War when vaccines began to appear. However, vaccination of children is very important and parents should ensure that their children are protected in this regard. Childhood illness is very traumatic for both parent and child. The fear of such illness is also a big burden and, if the objective risk of death is small, it is nonetheless real.

Cancer has been under intensive medical attack for the past few decades. Progress is claimed in the fight against cancer by pointing to the fact that the average interval between cancer diagnosis and death has increased significantly in recent years. However, this effect may be explained, at least partially, by the fact that the disease is now usually diagnosed at an earlier stage than previously. Although some cancers respond well to treatment, for example the relatively rare cancers of childhood, age-adjusted cancer mortality statistics for the USA show little change over the past fifty years.

It is not my purpose here to support claims that medicine is of little value. There are many things that medicine can do very well. Chief amongst these, in my opinion, is the repair of things that are mechanically broken in the body and the surgical removal of things that are either causing obstruction or are not functioning properly. Modern medicine can greatly improve the quality of life. Examples range from the soothing of an itch to the control of serious mental illness by a mind altering drug. Modern maternity hospitals ensure that infant or maternal death during childbirth are rare events indeed nowadays in developed countries. Immunisation relieves childhood of the distressing experience of many infectious diseases and undoubtedly saves lives. But it is not as clear as is widely assumed that medicine has played such a dominant part in improving life expectancy.

Neither is there conclusive evidence to show that improved nutrition or better hygiene standards are responsible for improving life expectancy. For example, as Sagan recounts, it has been noted that in past ages, when general life expectancy was low, members of royal families also lived short lives. It can be safely assumed that they did not lack for adequate nutrition. Also, research has pretty well established at this stage that a meagre diet, once it is above a certain minimum level, promotes rather than hinders longevity. On the question of improved hygiene, it has been noted that, once mortality rates from certain infectious diseases began to decline two hundred years ago, this decline continued despite prolonged periods of deterioration in hygiene standards associated with the development of urban slums.

So to what does Leonard Sagan attribute the remarkable improvement in average life expectancy over the last one hundred and fifty years? As life expectancy improved, average family size decreased, and positive and loving interest in children's welfare increased. In past ages, children were begot largely out of a sense of duty—they tended to be regarded as property assets and strict discipline and obedience were emphasised. The recognition that childhood is a special stage of development that should be nurtured with loving care is historically a recent development.

Children that are loved and looked after thrive, both physically and mentally, compared to children that do not receive such care. Many studies demonstrate this. Also the modern man or woman feels much more secure in the world than people did in ages past, when no average person could feel he had much control over his life. This must have produced incomparably greater stress than the average person will encounter today. Imagine how you would feel as you buried your child while at the same time glancing nervously over your shoulder to check how your hut and your crops were coping with the uncontrollable floods. Makes the modern rat race look pretty tame, doesn't it? Again, it is well known that feelings of hopelessness and helplessness are bad both for physical and mental health.

The argument in a nut shell, then, is that the enhanced self-esteem, self-confidence and feeling of security that has been nurtured in people over the past two hundred years has improved natural resistance to debilitation and disease and has been largely responsible for modern increased life expectancy. If this is the case, it follows that society will be much more successful at promoting positive health and ensuring further improved life expectancy by providing all the necessary supports for secure and happy family life, rather than by throwing ever increasing resources at high technology medicine and allowing long established State and other supports for the family to be eroded.

In this respect some current trends are worrying. High rates of breakdown in marriage and of children born to unwed teenage mothers are widespread in some countries. We have nothing to be complacent about in Ireland. At present forty-five per cent of first births here are extra marital. Within the EU, outside Scandinavia, this figure is exceeded only by France and Britain. Many of the extra marital first births in Ireland are to single mothers who are not in stable relationships with the fathers. While it is undoubtedly possible for both mother and child to prosper without the presence or assistance of the father, it is equally true that, on average, the odds are stacked against such an outcome.

Human Ageing and Human Lifespan

I often receive invitations to subscribe to American health magazines. The advertising blurb accompanying a typical offer confidently exclaims: 'three minutes a day to a 120-year lifespan'. You are advised to consume large amounts of vitamin and mineral dietary supplements during these vital daily minutes. You are also promised that this daily three-minute munch will ensure robust health, including a vigorous sex life—you can literally become 'the oldest swinger in town'.

Such advertising inevitably prompts many questions. Is the process of gradually declining vigour in old age, culminating in death, inevitable? If so, is it nevertheless feasible to significantly extend human lifespan beyond the current familiar limit? How much biomedical research should be invested in this area?

Is death inevitable for humans? Insofar as present knowledge goes, the answer is yes. For some simple organisms, things are different. In a certain sense, many single-celled organisms neither age nor die. For example, under optimum environmental conditions an amoeba grows and, when it is ready, simply divides in two. In turn, the progeny also grow and divide in two. In this way the first amoeba attains a sort of immortality—at no stage can you say it has passed away. On the other hand, more complicated biological organisms go through the irreversible sequence of birth, growth, senescence and death.

The death of the body seems to be as natural as birth. Death within a limited period after birth ensures turnover of the species and allows evolution by natural selection to proceed with some efficiency. If, on the other hand, organisms didn't die and continued to procreate, those species with no, or few, natural predators would quickly grow in numbers and crowd out most other species.

Turnover is a basic characteristic of life. Whenever nature presents a face of apparent constancy, this invariably masks an underlying dynamic equilibrium. Thus, the molecules in our cells are continually being broken down and replaced. In many of our tissues, whole cells are continually dying off and being replaced. For example, every second, two and a half million worn-out red blood cells are removed from your circulation and broken down. At the whole population level, constant species number simply reflects a balance between birth rate and death rate. Death is part of life.

Different animal species have different lifespans. A mayfly lives for one day. A spider lives for one year. A mouse lives for three years. A squid lives for four years. A rat lives for six years. A cat or dog can live for up to twenty-five years. A horse can live for forty years. An elephant can live for seventy years. A human being can live for one hundred and twenty years. Some tortoises can live for one hundred and fifty years. Plants easily hold the record—some trees can live for more than four thousand years.

As a general rule, among mammals, larger species live longer than smaller ones. This may be due in part to the slower metabolism (body chemistry) of the larger animals. The metabolic theory of ageing holds that small mammals tick over faster, burn rapidly and live for a shorter time than large mammals which live longer at a more sedate pace. To use a mechanical analogy, if you take two engines and constantly run one fast and hot and the other one at a slower rate, the faster running engine will grow smoky and will burn itself out well before the slower running engine.

There are exceptions to the simple rule that lifespan is proportional to rate of metabolism. For example, some birds with high metabolic rates live longer than mammals three times their size. Consequently there are several other theories of ageing. The oldest theory holds that senescence results simply from wear and tear. Cells taken from old animals and examined under the electron microscope show obvious signs of 'wear and tear' compared to the cells from a young animal.

But the wear and tear theory doesn't explain everything either. In some Third World countries, where life is hard and medicine a luxury, death rates in infancy and youth are high, but, once a person reaches mature adulthood, life expectancy can be as good as in developed countries. There appears to be an inner biological clock which determines the rate at which we age and sets a limit on our lifespan.

But it might be argued that, if we live long enough, we will each develop a disease, such as heart disease, and this is what eventually terminates most lives. In other words, if medicine could abolish disease, would people live indefinitely? I'm afraid not. It appears that there is such a thing as a 'natural death'. One American study reported that thirty per cent of autopsies, carried out on people who were at least eighty-five when they died, could identify no cause of death. These people seemed to have simply died of old age.

To return to the analogy of the two engines. The heavily used engine wears out faster and dies sooner than the lightly used one. But consider an alternative scenario in which the heavily used engine is regularly treated to comprehensive repair and maintenance. This would obviously greatly extend its lifespan. Living cells also have a repair mechanism whereby the essential genetic material that controls day-to-day activities in the cell is maintained in good working order. However, the repair mechanism itself becomes less reliable as the organism ages and this results in the gradual accumulation of genetic mistakes. Eventually it can be envisaged that the cumulative effects of genetic mistakes, mechanical wear and tear and metabolic burn-out conspire to end the life of the organism.

Until recent times, most people everywhere died young. On average, ancient Romans lived no more than twenty or thirty years. Two hundred years ago, the average person would hope to live to forty. Average life expectancy in Ireland today is about seventy-six years. One must distinguish between life expectancy and maximum lifespan. In ages past, average life expectancy was much lower because of uncontrollable disease, high infant mortality and powerful psychological factors (see page 130). But I am not aware of any evidence that the maximum lifespan attainable by humans in past ages, in those people fortunate enough to escape disease and to be equipped with robust psychological health, was much less than presently attainable lifespans. Over the past two hundred years, average life expectancy has been slowly rising towards a maximum lifespan ceiling, which is probably genetically determined and no greater than about one hundred and twenty years.

Future advances in molecular biology may make it possible to extend human lifespan. Much research effort is afoot, particularly in the USA, aimed at slowing down the ageing process. Supplementing the diet with large amounts of Vitamin E is widely promoted as a way to slow down metabolic burnout. It is extremely unlikely that it will ever become possible to broaden human lifespan indefinitely—to achieve immortality. Even if this could ever be achieved, it is doubtful if it would be desirable, either biologically, medically, ethically or psychologically.

In any event, there are several uncomplicated ways presently available to us to achieve at least a measure of immortality. First of all, if you are a religious person you may have no problem at all with the concept of immortality, since you will believe that you have an immortal soul. But even if you are not religious you can still aspire to achieve a measure of immortality, either by having some of your characteristics transmitted to future generations through your descendants, or even by having a memory of your existence preserved by posterity as a result of making a major contribution during your lifetime. But, of course, there will always be people who feel like Woody Allen when he was asked: 'Mr Allen, how would you like to achieve immortality?' He replied: 'By living forever'.

Cancer: Prevention is Better than Cure

We know a lot of the causes of many types of cancer and these causes are avoidable. Cancer is largely a preventable disease. However, the main focus of the medical campaign against cancer has been aimed at finding a cure for this disease. Cancer prevention has not been nearly so highly emphasised. Research aimed at curing cancer has thrown up much valuable information, but has failed in its primary goal. While efforts to find a cure should continue, it is now high time to switch the emphasis in the struggle against cancer in the direction of prevention. (I will mostly quote American statistics in this chapter, since we only recently established a National Cancer Registry in Ireland.)

Cancer is mainly a disease of the aged. Elderly people are now more numerous and, because of this fact alone, cancer is more common today than it was earlier this century. It is therefore essential to discuss cancer trends in terms of age-adjusted rates. Such rates tell us how well we are doing against cancer, taking into account the fact that the absolute number of cancer deaths is going up because of other factors that influence longevity.

Over the course of this century most diseases have declined in the West, and some have disappeared. Cancer has continued to increase. Age-adjusted death rates from cancer have slowly increased in the USA from 0.8 deaths per 1,000 population per year in 1900 to about 1.3 deaths per 1,000 per year today. Much of this increase is due to cigarettes. Respiratory cancer death rates (age-adjusted) have increased from about 0.07 per 1,000 per year in 1940 to about 0.4 per 1,000 per year today. Cancer has become a modern plague. In 1994, it is estimated that cancer killed 538,000 Americans, more than double the number killed in the Second World War. One in three of us alive today will contract cancer and one in five of us will die from cancer.

The industrialised countries of the world have been seriously worried about cancer since the 1930s. In 1971, American President Richard Nixon initiated a new campaign against cancer—a 'War on Cancer'. The campaign was launched with typical American optimism and enthusiasm. After all, there was good reason to think that a country smart enough to put a man on the Moon could also eradicate cancer.

The war on cancer focussed primarily on curing the disease. Massive resources have been poured into the campaign. To date the National Cancer Institute, founded in the 1930s, has put more than twenty-nine billion dollars into cancer research. Despite the intensification of the effort since 1971, relatively little progress has been made generally in cancer treatment, although there has been a significant improvement in treatment of cancer in childhood. The five year survival rates for most cancers (including lung, breast, colon and stomach) are little better now than they were twenty years ago.

Difficult as it is to admit, the facts show that the medical war on cancer has been a qualified failure. Why has this huge effort produced such disappointing results? In my opinion the answer is because the campaign has concentrated so heavily on cure rather than prevention. The traditional medical approach in the West has been to concentrate on curing disease rather than on preventing it. Subjects such as nutrition, environmental policy and public health are neglected in medical school in favour of training in curative practices such as surgery and radiology.

Medical research was very successful historically in finding cures for the major infectious diseases. The nineteenth-century German bacteriologist, Robert Koch, showed that TB is caused by the tubercle bacillus, anthrax by the anthrax bacillus and cholera by the bacterium *Vibrio cholerae*. Antibiotics were developed to fight these germs and eventually vaccines were developed enabling millions to live free of the fear of these terrible diseases. The idea of 'one disease, one germ' became firmly established in the medical mind.

In the early years of cancer research much effort was expended on searching for the virus that causes cancer, until it was realised that, unlike the major infectious diseases, cancer is not caused by a unique single agent. There would be little wrong in an all-out attempt to cure cancer at the expense of instituting a comprehensive prevention programme, if the prospects for success offered reasonable odds. But cancer is fundamentally different in many ways from the infectious diseases—in the way it can grow inside the body for thirty years or more without betraying its presence, in the way it attacks the body and in the way it gets around the normal defences of the body. By the 1970s cancer specialists knew they were dealing with an enemy far more resourceful than TB or cholera. At the same time, many substances known to cause cancer (carcinogens) had been identified, thereby justifying an all-out preventive campaign. However, cancer prevention has little prestige associated with it. Prevention is not likely to launch a medical research career on the high road to Stockholm and a Nobel Prize.

It is widely agreed that cancer is largely a preventable disease. The causes have been known for a considerable time. For example, smoking cigarettes, inhaling high levels of radon, inhaling asbestos fibres and various other dusts, unprotected sunbathing and various pesticides all cause cancer. Also a high intake of fat and a low intake of fibre are associated with an increased risk of cancer. Many of the cancers we suffer from are caused by bad personal habits and most of the remainder are caused by dirty industries and poor government regulations.

If we stopped smoking cigarettes, ensured that radon levels in our homes were low, ate balanced diets, avoided unprotected sunbathing and kept ourselves aerobically fit, cancer rates would fall dramatically. For example, about one quarter of all cancer deaths are caused by cigarettes, mostly lung cancers.

Of course, it must be admitted that an effective preventive programme would be difficult to implement. The experience with cigarettes shows this. At this stage 'the dogs in the street' know that cigarette smoking causes lung cancer and heart disease. Nevertheless, today, twenty years after the introduction of widespread public education programmes, young people, particularly girls, still take up smoking in large numbers.

On the other hand, while adopting a blasé attitude towards cigarettes where a large objective risk exists, people can display an inordinate dread of other agents, such as routine emissions from nuclear power plants, where evidence of danger is nebulous. When deciding on the acceptability or non-acceptability of risks there are a number of attitude factors that determine people's decisions. The most important attitude factors are:

- n whether or not I see a benefit in taking the risk
- n whether or not I control the situation
- n whether or not I understand the risk
- n whether or not the risk is familiar
- n whether or not the risk is voluntary
- n whether or not I trust those responsible.

If I feel several of these negative attitude options towards some risk (e.g. if I feel the risk is involuntary), I will find the risk to be unacceptable. If I feel several of the positive attitudes in the list, the risk will be acceptable.

Much more effort and resources must be expended in order to ensure the efficacy of preventive programmes. Research is needed on the best way to ensure that public health programmes can get around attitude problems. Money should be diverted in this direction without delay. It will be far better spent than endlessly chasing after the latest super expensive cancer treatment machine.

Cancer and Chemicals in the Environment

A colleague recently said to me: 'Cancer has become a desperate scourge. In my own locality I know one or two people with cancer on every road. And, no wonder. We don't know what we are eating nowadays. Our food is full of chemicals.' These sentiments are common, but widely respected studies estimate that, overall, pollution accounts for only one per cent of human cancers.

Cancer is a major problem. One in three of us will contract cancer and one in five of us will die from cancer. It is mainly a disease of the aged. Elderly people are now more numerous in the population than earlier this century and, because of this fact alone, cancer is more common today. When discussing cancer trends, it is essential to speak in terms of age-adjusted rates. These rates, that take into account the fact that absolute numbers of cancer deaths are increasing because of increased longevity, tell us how well overall we are doing against cancer.

The feeling is widespread that deaths from cancer are greatly increasing, but this feeling is wrong. With the exception of deaths from respiratory cancer, largely caused by cigarettes, age-adjusted cancer death rates are now slowly falling. It is true that cancer incidence rates have been increasing for some types of cancer, for example prostate cancer, but much of this increase is accounted for by improvements in detection and diagnosis.

An agent that can cause cancer is called a carcinogen. A chemical is tested for carcinogenic potential by administering it to rats at near toxic doses and following up to see if cancer develops. About half of all chemicals tested, whether natural or synthetic, are carcinogenic at these doses. There is good reason to suspect that many chemicals are carcinogenic only at these very high doses. This is not taken into account by the testers who take a positive result to unambiguously identify a carcinogen whose potential to cause cancer is assumed to be proportional to dose, decreasing to zero risk only at zero dose. However, if it is true that many chemicals are carcinogenic only at high does, this philosophy of risk assessment greatly exaggerates the danger at the very low doses to which the public is exposed.

Bruce Ames, the widely respected American biochemist, points out that the great bulk of the chemicals ingested by humans is natural, both by weight and number. Ames asserts that the widespread suspicion that a large fraction of all cancers is caused by synthetic industrial chemicals is mistaken. (See 'The Causes and Prevention of Cancer: The Role of Environment' in: *The True State of the Planet*, R. Bailey (Ed.) The Free Press, 1995.)

There is widespread concern about residual pesticides in food. According to Ames, 99.99 per cent of the pesticides in food are natural, present in plants to repel insects and other predators. We cannot eat food without ingesting these natural pesticides, half of which test positive as rodent carcinogens. Public and regulatory interest focuses on the 0.01 per cent that are synthetic pesticides. However, reducing our exposure to this tiny fraction, while ignoring the 99.99 per cent background levels, cannot be expected to reduce cancer rates.

If nobody smoked, drank alcohol or ingested a synthetic chemical, and if everybody ate a perfect diet and adopted a perfectly healthy lifestyle in all respects, would cancer disappear? Unfortunately not, but the incidence of cancer would go down by perhaps eighty per cent. Our cells are chemical machines. They work well but they are not perfect. Mistakes are made and damage is caused by unavoidable background agents such as natural radiation. The cell has mechanisms to repair damage and to neutralise ingested natural plant pesticides but, over time, mistakes and damage build up. This natural ageing causes an unavoidable level of background cancer.

Causation of cancer in the developed world can be divided between the following factors—diet accounts for about one third of cancer risks, smoking accounts for about one third of the risk, and the remainder can be attributed to hormone imbalance, pollutants in air, infections, some high risk occupations, overexposure to sun, hereditary factors and background cancers.

Even a cursory glance at the causation factors shows that most cancer is preventable. As regards diet, the standard recommendation of eating, in moderation, a wide variety of foods distributed across the four food groups is very good advice. In particular one should eat lots of fruit and vegetables. The quarter of the population with the lowest intake of fruit and vegetables has twice the cancer rate of the quarter with the highest intake. Vigorous physical exercise also reduces risk of cancer. There is some evidence that animal fat and red meat increase incidence of some cancers, so it is best to watch fat intake and to eat white meat and fish as well as red meat. Excessive intake of alcohol is a risk factor for some cancers.

Smoking tobacco is responsible for up to one third of all cancer deaths. Smoking also causes about one quarter of all heart disease. Everybody knows that cigarettes are deadly. The number of people who continue to smoke and, in particular, the numbers of young people who take up smoking is a major scandal.

Synthetic air pollutants are much feared by the public but the evidence is that they present only a small risk. Indoor air quality is of greatest concern as people spend ninety per cent of their time indoors. The most important carcinogen in air is probably the natural radioactive gas radon. It seeps into houses from the underlying soil and it may cause up to ten per cent of lung cancers. The Radiological Protection Institute of Ireland (RPII) has surveyed the country in order to identify areas with high levels of indoor radon. Parts of Galway, Mayo, Clare, Cork, Wicklow, Carlow, Wexford and Louth have been identified as high radon areas, although individual high radon houses can occur anywhere in the country (see chapter on radon on page 189). A test to measure radon in your house is available from the RPII. High radon levels can be remedied for £500–£1,500.

The long expensive search for a cure for cancer has been largely fruitless. Cancer prevention works and it costs little or nothing. Eat sensibly with plenty of fruit and vegetables, don't smoke, don't drink to excess, treat the sun with caution and take plenty of exercise. And finally, be happy—it reduces risk factors for all diseases.

Cynicism is Bad for your Health

It is well established that people with Type A personalities have a higher probability of suffering heart attacks than people with Type B personalities. The Type A personality displays a range of characteristics that generally produce stress. Research in the 1980s showed that, of all of these characteristics, cynicism is the most toxic. It follows, therefore, that being sensibly trusting of each other not only makes for a more contented and happier life, but is also good for our health. Generally, stress is a causative factor in a majority of illnesses and it is therefore important to know how to minimise it.

The fact that the mind can affect the body has been known since ancient times. However, the psychosomatic dimensions of disease have been neglected by modern medicine. Its history has been dominated by the 'one disease, one germ' doctrine (i.e. every disease is caused by a single physical factor). This approach was very productive in many instances and resulted in the conquest of the major infectious diseases, such as pneumonia. However, it is obviously not a very fruitful doctrine with which to confront diseases of multifactorial causation, and it is of little or no use for dealing with mind–body interactions in disease. As a consequence, medicine has made very slow progress in dealing with the two major killer diseases of modern civilisation—cancer and heart disease—both of multifactorial causation and, at least in the case of heart disease, having a pronounced psychosomatic dimension.

In 1959, two American cardiologists, Meyer Friedman and Ray Rosenman, defined the Type A personality. The classic Type A personality exhibits three main characteristics. He or she:

- n is highly competitive and ambitious
- n speaks rapidly and interrupts others frequently
- n is cynical and seized by hostility and anger with uncommon

frequency.

In short, he or she is constitutionally unable to sit back and relax. People who do not exhibit these pronounced personality characteristics are classed as Type B personalities.

Soon afterwards, large-scale survey studies showed that Type A personalities were much more likely to develop heart disease than Type B personalities. The question now was: do each of the three characteristics of the Type A personality contribute equally to predisposing the individual to heart disease, or is the effect mainly due to one or two of these characteristics? Further survey studies showed that the main toxic element in the Type A personality resides in the area of hostility. Careful analysis of this area more precisely defines it as cynicism, i.e. a contemptuous distrust of human nature and motives. Oscar Wilde, in *Lady Windermere's Fan*, defined the cynic as: 'A man who knows the price of everything and the value of nothing'. Another quote, attributed to H. L. Mencken, defines the cynic as: 'A man who, when he smells flowers, looks around for a coffin'.

How can a mental attitude lead to the development of atherosclerosis? Atherosclerosis is a disease characterised by the laying down of fatty deposits on the inner walls of arteries, thereby constricting them and, if the condition progresses, eventually leading to a heart attack. A cynical person, mistrustful of the world, is constantly on his or her guard—in other words, in a constant state of arousal. Such a person will naturally secrete a higher level of certain hormones into the blood than will a person who mostly spends his or her time in a less aroused state. These hormones, principally adrenalin, cortisol and testosterone, exert a constant wear and tear effect on body organs and mobilise fat into the blood from fat depots. A person who tends to oversecrete these hormones will regularly establish blood fat levels that favour the laying down of fatty deposits in the arteries.

I don't know to what extent the development of cynicism in a person is determined by hereditary factors. However, it seems very likely that cynicism must be, to some extent at least, a learned attitude. Parents and teachers can therefore help children to grow into happier and healthier adults by teaching them to adopt sensible, trusting attitudes towards the world.

Unfortunately the ill-effects of the stressful lifestyle of the Type A personality are not confined to heart disease. It is reckoned that stress is a contributory causative factor in about seventy per cent of all illnesses. In addition to heart disease, these illnesses include disorders of the gastrointestinal tract (e.g. ulcers and irritable bowel syndrome), asthma, rheumatoid arthritis, eczema, acne, psoriasis, alopecia areata and various mental disorders.

A particularly unfortunate development in recent decades has been the increase in levels of stress experienced by students in all three levels of education. There are two components contributing to this increase—one is under our own control and is probably the major factor; the other is intrinsic to the system and is, to a large extent, beyond our control.

Our educational and social systems have intrinsic characteristics that produce more stress for students now than in the past. Lack of good immediate employment prospects for 18–20 year olds and technological changes in the workplace have combined to devalue the worth of the Leaving Certificate as a passport to a job. The main value of the Leaving Certificate nowadays is as an entry ticket to third level education. And of course the 'quality' of the seat in university to which your ticket will admit you is determined by the number of points you achieve in your Leaving Certificate.

Our educational system is competitive and inherently stressful. This has always been so. There is little we can do in the short term about much of the endemic stress in education and it is unwise to dwell much on the matter. Mark Twain had some good advice in this regard: 'If you have to swallow a frog, don't look at it too long'.

The factors I described previously have increased pressures on young people in recent times, but not to the extent that is commonly claimed. A bigger contributor to increased stress, in my opinion, is the compulsion felt by so many, particularly the media, to focus unrelentingly on the 'race' for points. Senior cycle secondary education has been made miserable for so many teenagers and their parents by this pounding emphasis on the 'points race'. The pressure prevents so many (perhaps most) children from choosing careers they naturally like and forces them to pick the 'best' career they can 'win'. And, of course the most desirable careers are a handful of professions perceived to be the best paid. People forget that a person will automatically make a success, in every sense, of work he or she likes.

Stress is an enemy of health and happiness. We should all consciously strive to manage stress in our lives. A very good book which outlines a sensible blueprint for students that will enable them to negotiate a happy and productive path through second and third level education is *The Student: A Guide to Success in Second and Third Level Education*, by Doctors Mary Dineen and Breda McLeavey (Folens, 1992). Jesus Christ also gave us very good general advice a long time ago: 'Can any of you live a minute longer, by worrying about it? If you can't manage even such a small thing, why worry about the other things?'

Figure 1: A coloured woodcut from Martin Luther's Bible (1543) showing God as the architect of the universe, ordered as described by Ptolemy, with the Earth at the centre.

Figure 2: Pillar of Creation: This scene looks like a cloud formation viewed from an aircraft window. However, this cloud of gas and dust is 7,000 light years away and was photographed in the Hubble Space Telescope. The cloud pillar is about ten trillion kilometres tall. The wispy tendrils of gas and dust seen at the edge of the pillar are each as wide as our solar system. The telescope has detected new stars being born in these tendrils.

Figure 3: The fiery nuclear furnace of the Sun.

Evolution
The map of life

The first sign of life came from the sea almost one thousand million years ago: simple microscopic cells appeared which began to divide, creating conditions for the evolution of the plant and animal worlds. From that time on, very slowly . . .

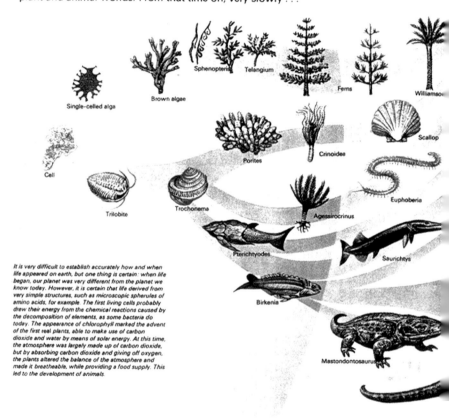

It is very difficult to establish accurately how and when life appeared on earth, but one thing is certain: when life began, our planet was very different from the planet we know today. However, it is certain that life derived from very simple structures, such as microscopic spherules of amino acids, for example. The first living cells probably drew their energy from the chemical reactions caused by the decomposition of elements, as some bacteria do today. The appearance of chlorophyll marked the advent of the first real plants, able to make use of carbon dioxide and water by means of solar energy. At this time, the atmosphere was largely made up of carbon dioxide, but by absorbing carbon dioxide and giving off oxygen, the plants altered the balance of the atmosphere and made it breatheable, while providing a food supply. This led to the development of animals.

Figure 4: Map of Life, showing how the various forms of life currently present on Earth are descended from the simple initial life-form that arose about 3.5 billion years ago.

Sigillaria

Lepidodendron

Cypridina

Limulus

Lemmatophora

Larch

Meduse

Murex

Oak tree

Crab

Grasshopper

Spider

Timarcha

Butterfly

Salamander

...trachus

Lamprey

Teleosteus

Frog

Coelacanth

Crow

Macropoma

Hesperomis

Neofiber

Archaeopteryx

Rhamphorynchus

Natalus

Dicerorhinus

Mammuthus primigenius

Horse

Hyracotherium

Dimetrodon

Proganochelidae

Crocodile

Australopithecus

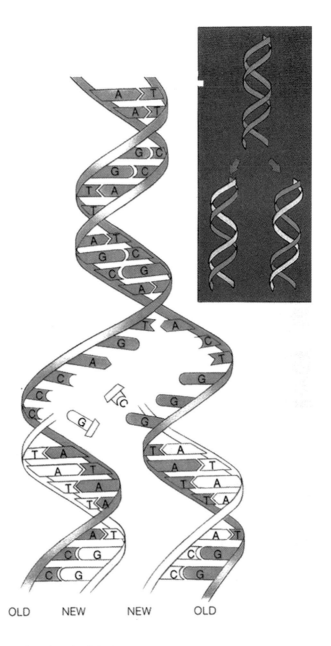

OLD   NEW   NEW   OLD

Figure 5; A short length of the long DNA molecule showing the two nucleotide chains wrapped around each other in double helix fashion and bonded together by attractive forces between the bases (A to T and G to C). The figure also illustrates how DNA duplicates itself during cell division. The original parent strand (shown in blue) duplicates itself when a new strand (yellow) is assembled on each of the two original strands.

Figure 6: Dolly and her lamb Bonnie

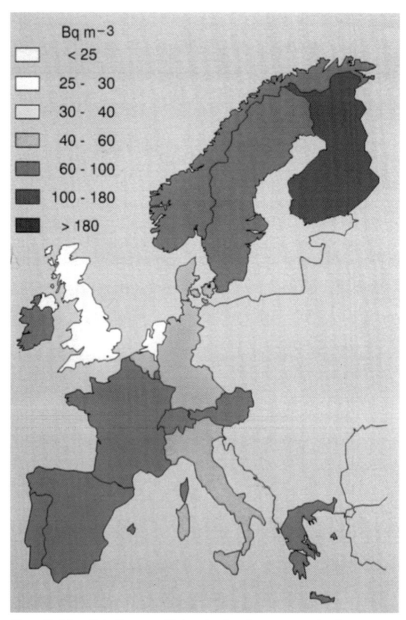

Figure 7: Map of the European Union showing the average national concentrations of indoor radon, measured in Becquerels per cubic metre (Bqm^{-3}). The data was compiled by the EU from information supplied by the member states.

Alzheimer's Disease

Alzheimer's disease is a very distressing condition, both for the sufferer and for all those who care about the victim. Incidence of the disease is sharply increasing and there is no cure. However, great progress is being made in understanding the basic biochemistry of the condition. Much of this work has been carried out at the National Institute on Ageing in America under the direction of Zaven Khachaturian. It is hoped that effective treatments will be available soon, followed closely by a cure.

At least sixteen million people world-wide suffer from Alzheimer's disease (AD). Ireland has 33,000 cases of AD. Most cases develop after the age of sixty-five in people with no family history of the disease, although genetic factors predispose people to the disorder. AD is the leading form of dementia in the elderly, responsible for about half of all cases. A small number of cases of AD (two to seven per cent) are an early-onset variety and can afflict people as young as thirty. Early-onset AD is an inherited condition distinct from late-onset AD.

AD destroys the brain silently. Usually the first symptom to appear is forgetfulness. This is followed by severe loss of memory, confusion, uncoordinated movement, garbled speech, personality changes, hallucinations and mood swings. As the brain deteriorates, the rest of the body gradually closes down until, invariably, the victims are left incapable of caring for themselves. Death ensues somewhere between two and twenty years after the appearance of the first symptoms.

AD has existed since ancient times and writers have often described the typical symptoms. Shakespeare's King Lear, losing his memory and growing disoriented, is a well-known example. AD was defined as a distinct disease in 1906 by a German physician, Alois Alzheimer. He described a patient who presented with volatile behaviour, memory loss, disorientation, hallucinations and paranoia. After the death of the patient,

Alzheimer examined her brain and described the odd growths, called tangles and plaques, that are now considered the unambiguous fingerprint of AD. A protein called beta-amyloid protein forms sticky clumps at the core of the plaques in AD brain.

The sector of the population at greatest risk of AD are people aged eighty-five and over. This is the fastest growing population sector in developed countries. People are now also, on average, physically healthier at all ages than in the past. Therefore, not only are absolute numbers of AD victims on the increase, but the average duration of the disease is also increasing. Health care is very expensive and unless effective treatment or a cure for AD is forthcoming soon, society faces an enormous financial burden.

The brain is a very complex arrangement of interconnected nerve cells (the neurons). In the absence of brain disease the organ will continue to function well into the tenth decade of life. In AD, neurons gradually lose the ability to extract energy from glucose (the principal food for the brain) to carry out essential repairs and, eventually, to connect to other neurons. Neurons often die. It is not known what causes the brain systems to deteriorate in AD.

Acetylcholine is a chemical that is necessary in the transmission of electrical signals from one neuron to another and research has shown that neurons containing acetylcholine play an important role in memory. The first breakthrough in understanding the biochemistry of AD was made in 1976 when it was shown that an enzyme necessary to make acetylcholine was deficient in AD brains.

Later work in the 1980s and 1990s identified genes responsible for the early-onset form of AD and genes that predispose people to develop the much commoner late-onset AD. The identification of genes opens the possibility of genetic testing. However, a positive test for the late-onset predisposing gene does not necessarily mean a person will get AD. One could also question, on ethical grounds, the value of a genetic test in a situation where there is no cure for the disease.

AD is a complex disorder and it is likely that genetic and environmental factors interact to initiate the process. Some years ago there was a widespread feeling that ingestion of aluminium played a significant role in AD. This hypothesis no longer finds favour with the majority of researchers in the field. The three systems of neuronal intercommunication, energy metabolism of glucose and neuronal repair work together to keep the brain healthy. It is probable that a disruption of any of these systems, whether caused by imbalanced nutrition, toxins, trauma or infection could start off degenerative changes culminating in AD.

To my knowledge only two drugs are on the market to treat AD. Both slow the breakdown of acetylcholine in the brain and thereby help communication between damaged neurons. The drugs slow the rate of deterioration in some patients but cannot prevent the final victory of AD. Recent research findings on the protein that accumulates to form the characteristic plaques and tangles in the AD brain holds the promise of the development of a more effective drug to treat AD.

If you are in your sixties and have noticed that your memory is not what it used to be, should you worry that AD may be developing? No. Memory performance in everybody slowly declines from the age of twenty. The decline becomes more noticeable beyond the age of sixty but there is a considerable range of normal variation. With any luck at all, your mind will remain clear for the entire duration of your earthly journey.

Diet and Nutrition

Sensible Eating is Simple

It has been remarked that the average American, looking down on a plate of bacon and eggs, doesn't see bacon and eggs—he sees death. This statement may be an exaggeration, but it contains a substantial nugget of truth and it applies to Europeans as well as to Americans, although with somewhat less emphasis. Western society has developed an unhealthy preoccupation with diet. Many people have come to believe that choosing a nutritious diet requires much skill and knowledge and that wrong choices can easily be made which will have serious consequences. Luckily, the truth is to the contrary. The rules governing healthy eating are long established and simple to follow.

A healthy diet is composed of protein, carbohydrate, fat, vitamins and minerals, all in the right proportions and forms. Choosing a diet that will supply these nutrients in optimum proportions is very easy indeed. The choice is governed by the first and most important law of good nutrition and healthy living. This says that one should eat a diet that is consistently varied across the four major food groups. Adults are advised to eat, every day, four servings from the fruits and vegetables group, four from the bread and cereal grains group, two from dairy products group (for example, milk and cheese) and two from the meat and beans group (for example, meat, fish, poultry or eggs—peas, beans or nuts are alternatives). The choices from each group should be varied from day to day to avoid consumption of some foods to the exclusion of others. The term 'serving' has the ordinary everyday meaning. For example, a serving of apples would be one medium apple, of cereal—a cupful, of milk—one glass, of peas/beans—one cupful, of vegetables— one cupful, of bread—two or three slices, of meat—three ounces, etc. Adults should also drink about four pints of water per day.

The second rule of good nutrition is to maintain a healthy weight.

You maintain appropriate body weight by consuming only enough food to balance the amount of energy expended. People who consume more calories than they need become overweight. For many this increases the chances of developing diabetes and hypertension, both of which are risk factors for heart disease. If you wish to know the optimum weight for your height, sex and body type (slender or thick-set), you can look it up in any good medical encyclopaedia or book on nutrition or diet, or you can ask your doctor.

The third rule is to carry out moderate amounts of aerobic exercise. This will not only maintain cardiovascular fitness but will also tend to depress the appetite. Exercise can take the form of walking, running, swimming or cycling. For example, a daily brisk three mile walk, done in fifty minutes, is sufficient to maintain a good level of fitness. If you are out of condition, you will have to gradually work up to this.

Much is made nowadays about the connection between dietary fat and heart disease. The evidence in favour of a positive correlation comes from epidemiological studies and laboratory evidence that large amounts of saturated fat and cholesterol in the diet can lead to elevated levels of serum cholesterol, which can accumulate in artery walls and cause clogging. However, the situation is not very straightforward. Dietary cholesterol does not always raise serum cholesterol—some people can consume large amounts of cholesterol and still maintain low serum cholesterol levels, whereas others accumulate the substance even on low fat diets. Other factors are also associated with atherosclerosis, such as cigarette smoking, blood pressure and diabetes.

Eating a consistently varied diet in moderation will ensure that disproportionate amounts of fat are not consumed. In my opinion, the average person need be concerned little further than this about fat. It is also wise to take sensible precautions, such as sparing the use of fats and oils in cooking, using small amounts of salad dressings and spreads, choosing vegetable oils high in unsaturated fat, trimming fat from meat, taking skin off poultry, using moderate amounts of sugar and using table salt very sparingly. All of this advice applies to the average healthy person. If special circumstances apply, for example high levels of blood cholesterol, you should take specialised advice on diet from your doctor.

There are few subjects about which so much popular misinformation is promulgated than food and diet. I will give two examples: 'The poor cannot afford nutritious diets' and 'some foods are "good", others are "bad"'. The simple truth regarding income and nutrition, it seems to me, is that if you can afford to buy food at all, you can buy food that is nutritious. Many foods in the four main groups are relatively inexpensive, such as beans, peas, milk, bread, eggs, some cereals, some cheeses, vegetables, some varieties of fish, rice and fruit in season. Meat is expensive, but remember that stewing steak is just as nutritious as fillet steak. If poor people eat less nutritious fare than better-off people, the immediate causes are not economic.

A simple-minded formula has gained currency in recent years to the effect that some foods are good and other foods are bad. For example, fish and high fibre foods are good, whereas red meat and butter are bad. It is felt that fibre is good because it can help to maintain a healthy gut and may lower blood cholesterol. On the other hand, foods rich in saturated animal fat may raise blood cholesterol and possibly lead to atherosclerosis. However, if one adheres to the first two principles of good dietary practice, adequate amounts of all essentials are assured and no individual elements are supplied in excess.

To single out individual foods as either good or bad is dangerous. It tends to make people overemphasise some foods and possibly cut other foods out altogether, even whole food groups. The result is an unbalanced and sub-optimal diet which can, in extreme cases, lead to severe problems. For example, take the recent case of a man who was so impressed with the nutritional qualities of bran that he ate copious amounts of it at every opportunity. A ball of bran eventually obstructed his intestine and an operation had to be performed to remove it.

What about take-away hamburgers and french fries? They tend to have a high fat and salt content and will unbalance the diet if eaten very frequently. Fast food is all right occasionally as a convenience, but it should be left at that.

Food advertisements now play on our obsession with diet, emphasising a connection between diet and health and between diet and a beautiful body. The message is 'eat brand X and you will not get disease Y' or 'eat brand X and you will look like this beautiful model' (ignore the fact that you are genetically shaped like a pear!). The aim of advertising is to sell product, not to educate the public or to improve public health. It widely disseminates half-truths and infects the public with anxieties about foods. The real truth about good nutrition and healthy living is simple and straightforward—variety, moderation and exercise. If we adopt these habits we can stop fretting over the nutritional value of every forkful that enters our mouths. Such a development would cause the food advertisers to fret, and wouldn't that be nice for a change!

Obesity: Causes and Solutions

Obesity is the term given to the condition of being excessively fat. Obesity is bad for health and, because the condition is generally perceived as physically unattractive, obese people often encounter discrimination and suffer from low self-esteem. The incidence of obesity is increasing in all developed countries. Both understanding its causes and developing strategies to deal with the condition are proving to be difficult problems to solve.

How is obesity defined? Body-mass index (BMI) is frequently used as an indicator. BMI is defined as the weight of a person in kilograms divided by the square of his or her height in metres. A common view holds that people with BMIs between 18 and 22 are the healthiest. This is a stringent criterion and, for example, fewer than 20% of Americans lie in that category (I have no figures for Ireland). According to this criterion, the ideal weight for a six foot tall person would lie between 132 and 162 pounds. Other research indicates that the healthiest BMI range is between 22 and 27. The commonest medical definition of obesity is a BMI greater than 27. In other words, if you are six feet tall and weigh more than 200 pounds, you are at risk.

Obesity is a major risk factor in disorders such as hypertension, osteoarthritis, cardiovascular disease and some forms of cancer, and it also plays a role in triggering non-insulin dependent diabetes. It is also well known that people who are perceived to be physically unattractive suffer a lot of social discrimination. This can sometimes have bizarre results. Recently, a Tennessee woman took legal action against a cinema when she was refused a seat. The cinema claimed she posed a fire hazard.

How do we gain weight? In overall terms, this is easy to understand. We take energy into our bodies in the form of food. If our various activities don't burn up all of this food energy, the balance is converted into fat and we gain weight. We burn up our food energy in three main ways. Firstly, we have to expend a certain amount of energy in order to digest and absorb the food. Secondly, we continually expend energy at a basic rate just by staying alive—energy is needed to pump blood, to breathe, to maintain body temperature, and so on. This is called the basal metabolic rate. Thirdly, we burn up energy when we exercise and do work. If you are an adult and you maintain a constant weight, this means that the energy expenditure in the three processes that I have described exactly balances the energy content of your food intake. If your energy expenditure were to decline you would gain weight, and if your energy expenditure were to increase, you would lose weight, assuming your food intake remains constant.

People who are obese obviously eat far more food than they burn up. Are there special factors that predispose some people to become obese? Clearly if the fundamental mechanisms that the body uses to burn up food energy are less efficient in some people than in others, the less efficient 'burners' will tend to be fatter. However, it turns out, rather surprisingly, that the three basic mechanisms for burning up food energy seem to be as efficient in obese people as in people of normal weight. It follows, therefore, that people who are obese simply eat more food than people of normal weight.

People have an in-built mechanism that produces a feeling of 'fullness' when an optimum amount of food, just adequate to meet physiological demand, has been ingested. Therefore, if you stop eating as soon as you feel full, you will not become overweight. The problem with obese people, however, seems to be that they must eat a lot more food than non-obese people in order to get the same feeling of fullness. Therefore, advising an obese person to stop eating as soon as he feels full can be a prescription for overeating.

So, how can you return to normal weight if you are obese? In the great majority of cases, the only feasible answer is to reduce the food intake. You might think that it would be possible to work on the other side of the equation and to burn off the food through physical exercise. However, physical exercise is not a very efficient way to burn up stored fat and the amount of exercise necessary to significantly reduce the weight of an obese person, given that the food intake remained high, would be very strenuous.

I used an exercise gymnasium for the first time recently. I worked up what I thought was a considerable sweat for thirty minutes on an exercise bicycle. The machine had a calorie-counter which measured the amount of energy burned up. I only got rid of the two half-coated chocolate biscuits that I had eaten after my lunch.

There are extreme measures that can be taken to reduce food intake. These include wiring the jaws together or surgically reducing the size of the stomach. These measures would only be used in cases where there is severe medical urgency to effect a guaranteed early weight loss. Such measures would certainly not be the first line of attack if you felt you were starting to develop a bit of a pot-belly! And so we come to the conventional answer for the average person, which is, of course, to go on a diet.

Diets are getting quite a bad reputation. In so many cases they just don't work. For so many people the efficiency of dieting is summed up in the Henny Youngman joke: 'My wife has been on a diet for weeks—all bananas and apples. She hasn't lost any weight, but you should see her climb a tree.' It isn't that dieting in itself is ineffective. The problem is that people will not stay on the diets. After a short period of disciplined eating and weight loss they go back to their old eating habits.

People who overeat are, by definition, somewhat obsessed with food. In my opinion, this preoccupation is the major part of the problem. The reason why dieting is so hard to stick with is that it further accentuates this focusing on food. You may be eating less but you are thinking about food more. The trick is to think less about food. If you can do this, it will be far easier to maintain a dieting regime. So, you have to focus outwards and occupy your mind with things other than your own 'problem'. What's needed is something that really grabs the interest. For some, a hobby or a sport will do the trick. Others may need to become involved in community affairs, charitable organisations or political affairs. It is also very important to take regular aerobic exercise. You feel much better when you are physically fit and strenuous exercise has a depressing effect on appetite.

You can look up information on ideal body weight for height and sex in any medical reference book. If you are obese you should take urgent action to reduce weight and to become aerobically fit. However, even with the best will in the world, some people find it extremely difficult, because of genetic predisposition, to bring their weight right down into the 'ideal' category. There is no need to worry about this. Once you are physically fit, there is no danger in being slightly chubby.

Unfortunately, modern advertising puts intense pressure, particularly on women, to achieve an idealised physical shape. This is just not possible for many people. It is also a waste of time. An attractive appearance is not embodied in an idealised physical shape. An attractive appearance is almost entirely to do with the glint in the eye, the healthy tone of the skin and, above all, the personality that shines through from the inner essence. Unfortunately, there is no known diet that will give you an attractive personality. Wherever that comes from, it's not from the box of diet cereal.

Why Exercise is Good for the Heart

I think it was Oscar Wilde who remarked: 'Whenever I feel like exercise, I lie down until the feeling passes'. The idea that strenuous exercise is good for you is a very modern development. We now know that physical exercise has many positive benefits, probably the most important of which is that it is good for the heart.

Heart attacks kill one in four people in industrially developed countries. Everyone knows that a heart attack means a failure of the heart, but most people don't understand why or how this failure comes about.

The body is composed of cells and every cell needs access to flowing blood in order to survive. The function of the heart is to pump blood around the body, through the arteries and veins, supplying oxygen and other nutrients to all the cells and removing waste products from them. The heart is primarily a blood-pumping muscle and the muscle cells are called myocytes. The myocytes contract and relax in a synchronous and automatic fashion causing the heart to beat, or pump, about seventy times per minute, thereby keeping the blood circulation flowing. The pressure wave accompanying each beat travels down the arteries and can be felt as a pulse. Over a seventy year lifespan, the human heart beats about two and a half billion times.

The heart operates as two pumps working in parallel. The right side of the heart receives oxygen depleted blood from all over the body and pumps it to the lungs for oxygenation. The left side of the heart receives oxygenated blood from the lungs and pumps it around the body.

The myocytes must also be supplied with blood, just like the cells of any other organ. This is achieved through the main coronary arteries that enter the walls of the heart, branching again and again, forming a complicated web of blood vessels—the coronary vasculature. The heart

162

cells must be supplied with a lot of blood. The heart uses between four and five per cent of total body blood flow but, on average, it only makes up 0.5 per cent of the body's weight. Only the brain comes close to the heart in its appetite for blood per unit mass of tissue.

The heart is particularly sensitive to having its blood supply interrupted. When a part of the heart loses its blood supply, it is said to become ischaemic. Its ability to work as a pump falls within seconds and fails within minutes. Ischaemia is usually caused when an artery that serves a particular area of the heart becomes clogged. Ischaemic heart disease is the underlying cause of most heart attacks.

The coronary network of blood vessels is very adaptable. It can grow and adapt itself to fit the needs of the body and can readapt and reshape itself to meet changed needs, provided there is appropriate vasculature to build on and time to do the building. The trigger that starts the growth of new vasculature is need. While an organism is growing, the extension of the vasculature is driven by the growth of the tissue that demands more blood. But, in a mature organism, the vasculature can still grow if it is prompted by a steady high demand for oxygen. The vasculature of the heart can be maintained and expanded by carrying out aerobic exercise which puts the heart under regular moderate strain.

The coronary arteries are particularly prone to developing the disease of atherosclerosis. This is a slowly developing condition in which fatty growths on the artery walls gradually constrict and choke off the flow of blood. The great majority of heart failures are associated with atherosclerosis, which causes the ischaemia described earlier. Atherosclerosis affects not only the heart, but also large and medium sized arteries throughout the body. For example, most strokes are caused by atherosclerosis in cerebral arteries.

The gradual narrowing of a coronary artery is likely to cause angina. This is a crushing chest pain that often feels like a band around the chest. It usually occurs when the subject starts a physically demanding activity—the narrowing artery doesn't allow sufficient blood flow to fuel the extra work of the heart. In cases of severe artery narrowing or blockage, a coronary artery bypass graft is often performed. The surgeon removes part of a vein or artery, usually the saphenous vein in the leg, and joins it to the blocked coronary artery before and after the blockage, creating a bypass. A patient may receive a single, double, triple or quadruple bypass, depending on how many main coronary arteries are blocked.

A normal youthful coronary vasculature has considerable reserve capacity to provide enhanced blood flow to meet the demands of sudden heavy activity. Atherosclerosis can gradually reduce this reserve capacity over the years to the point where, if the heart is suddenly called on to work at maximum effort, the vasculature cannot deliver the blood flow necessary to keep it working. This is when a spontaneous game of football with the grandchildren could have disastrous consequences.

The important reserve capacity of the vasculature of the heart can be slowly eroded over the years by atherosclerosis without sending out any warning signals. If one leads a sedentary lifestyle, the heart can retain sufficient reserve capacity to meet the very occasional sudden demand without going into distress. However, if atherosclerosis is developing, the day will probably come when a serious problem suddenly announces itself without prior warning. On the other hand, if as a young adult one cultivates a regular habit of moderate aerobic exercise, this will maintain a healthy reserve capacity in the vasculature of the heart and will also help to retard the progress of atherosclerosis.

Aspects of the Environment

Does Conservation Save or Squander?

There is virtually unanimous agreement across all sectors of society, from government to environmental pressure groups, that measures should be taken to conserve scarce resources. Energy is a prime example of a scarce resource. Governments encourage conservation in this area by subsidising citizens who use energy efficiently (remember the subsidy to defray the installation costs of back-boiler home central heating systems?) and by exhorting technologists to develop machinery that is energy efficient.

All of this seems to be sensible and also accords well with our traditional sense of thrifty behaviour—'A penny saved is a penny earned'. However, some economists argue that the basic nature of the economic system ensures that conservation measures designed to spare scarce resources frequently do not work—and sometimes have the opposite effect, leading to increased use of these resources. Such analysis is useful, but some prescriptions offered by economists call for unwarranted acts of faith in economic models. Also, on the issue of world population control, the advice offered by the economists is the complete opposite of the advice of biological scientists.

The American experience with the motor car over recent decades is cited as a case where seemingly sensible conservation measures did not work. Throughout the 1950s and 1960s, the average mileage per gallon achieved by the American motor car was fourteen. When OPEC quadrupled the price of petrol as a result of the 1973 Arab–Israeli War, the American Congress passed an Energy Conservation Act. Amongst other provisions, the Act called for the energy efficiency of American cars to rise gradually to 27.5 miles per gallon. As a result, American cars gradually improved in efficiency and, by 1989, the average mileage per gallon had increased to 20.5 miles—a forty-five per cent increase since the early 1970s.

All other factors remaining equal, petrol consumption should have dropped to sixty-five per cent of its original use. This did not happen, however. Between 1973 and 1992 the average volume of petrol used per day in American cars remained remarkably constant. The reason for this was that, despite an increase in the price of petrol, the improved efficiency of the engine made cars cheaper to run. Sales of motor cars increased, as did the average number of miles travelled per year by a motor car. The improved efficiency of the motor car lead to its greater use and, therefore, the overall consumption of petrol did not drop. Interestingly, efforts at conservation led to increased economic activity.

The free market, with its primary variables of supply and demand, the interaction of which determine commodity price, is a primary model of economic analysis. This type of analysis neatly explains the various interactions that led to the final outcome in the American attempt to conserve petrol. Economists view the free market mechanism as a thing of beauty which, if left to its own devices, is self-regulating. Some economists have such deep faith in the benign self-regulatory powers of the free market that they believe other independent parts of nature will co-operate with it in order to bring about a positive result.

Take, for example, the opinion of many influential economists on the best approach to conserve valuable metals. These metals are valuable because they are vital components in the manufacture of various essential products, such as the use of chromium in the manufacture of steel. It is argued that no artificial intervention should be made to conserve limited stocks of metal. The economic model predicts that if stocks become scarce, the price will rise and this will automatically reduce the use of the precious metal and will provide an incentive to discover new stocks of metal elsewhere. Even more importantly, the economists argue that the market place will now provide powerful incentives that will spur scientists and technologists to discover cheaper and widely available substitutes for the metal.

In my opinion, this analysis takes far too little account of the part that serendipity plays both in the discovery of new ore bodies and in the process of scientific discovery. Scientists cannot produce discoveries to

167

order. If they could, the Black Death would never have been the scourge of Europe, because inoculations would have been invented. Also, we would no longer fear cancer, because a cure would have been found twenty-five years ago. The economic analysis is flawed because important elements of it rely on chance. No matter how many past examples the economists may cite where new discoveries saved the day, there is no guarantee that this will happen in the future.

Many economists oppose the introduction of population control measures to stabilise burgeoning population numbers in Third World countries whose economies cannot even support present numbers. Their economic analysis predicts that economic development will solve the problems. Biologists, on the other hand, call for population control measures as a first step, claiming that further increase in population numbers will produce unacceptable environmental degradation. The economists accuse the biologists of making catastrophic predictions that have not been accurate in the past. The biologists, on the other hand, liken the environment to an aeroplane. The aeroplane is held together by thousands of rivets. You can remove some rivets and the aeroplane will still work. However, remove too many and it falls apart. The environment has already lost a lot of rivets.

George Bernard Shaw once remarked: 'If you laid all economists in the world end to end, they would not reach a conclusion'. However, today, many economists are reaching many conclusions about the best way to deal with the environment. Some of these conclusions are good, some are not. There is an urgent need for economists and scientists to come together to discuss conservation and environmental matters. Each discipline can offer enlightening insights and an emerging consensus would prevent either side from independently proposing incomplete and naïve solutions to the government.

Mother Nature Undisturbed

Recent decades have witnessed the rise of a widespread and vibrant enthusiasm for the protection of our natural environment. This general concern for the environment was born out of a concern about the negative effects of large-scale human and economic activities on the natural environment. The desire to live in a clean and healthy world is undoubtedly a good thing. However, we must endeavour to remain clear-headed while pursuing this noble end, so that we don't end up prescribing remedies that are useless—or worse.

In this regard I would like to discuss a notion that is widely suffused throughout the general environmental movement. This is the notion that the ideal state of nature is one that remains completely undisturbed by human activities. In this state, nature is believed to be balanced, self-regulating and idyllic—a virtual Garden of Eden. I am not happy with this notion for two reasons. Firstly, this picture of nature is not true to reality. Secondly, this view pictures humans as antagonistic to the natural world—as vandals whose activities must be policed and whose instincts are to cause damage.

The history of the natural world is a litany of change. Massive changes have occurred in the natural environment of the Earth since the planet was formed. Relative to the length of time biological life has existed on Earth (three and a half billion years), *Homo sapiens* has only been around for the merest blink of an eye—200,000 years. Enormous changes have taken place in the natural environment since life began on Earth and all of the major changes occurred before humankind even existed. Some of these changes had a devastating effect on many existing life forms.

The atmosphere of the early Earth contained no oxygen. Life therefore began as an anaerobe, that is as an organism capable of living without oxygen. (In fact, oxygen is a deadly poison for these anaerobic organisms.) After a while, a new form of life developed capable of directly harnessing the energy of the Sun to synthesise food and, in the process, liberating oxygen to the atmosphere. Oxygen levels gradually built up in the atmosphere and the high ozone layer was formed (ozone is a form of oxygen). The oxygen in the atmosphere killed off most anaerobic forms of life, which were replaced by new forms of life capable of using molecular oxygen. Also, the newly formed ozone layer absorbed much of the incoming deadly ultraviolet light from the Sun thereby allowing most of the surface of the Earth to carry life.

The entire subsequent history of the natural world is an unbroken litany of change. On the biological side, new species of life arose, developed and spread into every habitable niche on the Earth. Great natural changes occurred from time to time, for example changes in climate. The Earth has experienced several ice ages. Some of the natural changes that occurred had a devastating effect on many biological species. There have been several mass extinctions of biological species.

The Earth itself is constantly changing. The Earth's outer crust is cracked to form several great plates that move slowly about on the underlying molten layers. Where these great plates collide or slide against each other, mountains are thrown up and earthquake activity and volcanoes are generated. Everywhere, and at all times, the natural world is changing.

The widespread deference to the idea that 'nature knows best', even when this is presented in technical scientific terminology such as in ideas of equilibrium and ecological climax, is often based less on a real knowledge of how the natural world operates than on a hankering after ideas inherited from eighteenth-century romantics. The romantics celebrated naturalness in all its forms—for example primitive man and untouched nature—as a reaction to what they thought were the overcivilising forces in modern society. These ideas gained strength during nineteenth-century industrialisation. However, it wasn't until recent decades that ideas developed in this mode of thinking, such as steady state nature, were put to empirical tests—and in many cases they didn't stand up.

Take, for example, the concept of maximum sustainable yield which, in fact, has something of a scientific basis. This is based on an equation that produces an S-shaped growth curve and describes the growth of a population of organisms under constant conditions, beginning with a small number of organisms and multiplying to an upper limit known as the carrying capacity, set by the conditions. The S-shaped growth curve can be observed if you put a few fruit flies into a bottle, maintain a constant food supply and environment and watch the population increase. The largest population that can be reproduced indefinitely— the maximum sustainable yield—is half the carrying capacity, according to a simple calculation.

The precision of the S-shaped curve had a powerful appeal for people who managed natural resources. But uncritical acceptance of the concept led to many problems. For example the Peruvian anchovy fishery was once the largest in the world. In 1970, this fishery yielded eight million tons of anchovies as in previous years; two years later the catch dropped by seventy five per cent. The fishery had been managed throughout this period to produce the maximum sustainable yield. It took many years for this fishery to slowly recover.

The moral is that lessons learned from simple systems in the laboratory often do not translate well to a natural ecological system. Ecosystems are extremely complex, made up of a huge number of interdependent organisms and factors. If one element shifts slightly, the whole system can change—for example, a fishery can collapse. In fact, such a system is the embodiment of change. This is true on every level—climate, distribution of species, rate of extinction of species. Constancy does not exist in the biosphere.

So, what is the message? Is it that it doesn't much matter what we do as human beings, because nature is changing anyway? Certainly not. Clearly ozone depletion, the enhanced greenhouse effect and acid rain are bad things and we must strive to reverse the conditions that produce them. But in dealing with the environment we must appreciate three things.

Firstly, we are part of nature ourselves and not a form of alien vandal. Seeing ourselves as set apart absolves us of true responsibility.

Secondly, although we know a certain amount about how ecosystems work, there is much more we don't know and we should be wary of working to rigid formulae. Thirdly, nature is not a law, like the law of gravity. It is a story and the story is not over. There is no given original state—a Garden of Eden—against which we can judge our 'fall', or to which we can return.

Perhaps at this stage all we can do, and the best thing we can do, is to think of nature as a garden and humankind as the gardener. We must cultivate our garden cautiously using our experience as well as scientific knowledge to ensure, as best we can, that our garden remains healthy, fruitful and beautiful.

Absolute Safety

Demands are frequently made by environmental groups for standards of safety that, in effect, carry a zero level of risk. A zero level of risk is impossible to achieve in any sphere and such demands are therefore unreasonable. These demands can also force the concentration of all the available but limited safety resources into certain areas targeted by environmental groups in an attempt to eliminate small residual risks, at the expense of ignoring larger risks in non-targeted areas.

Picture a typical scene. An environmental activist and a technical expert are publicly debating the safety of a commercial product. The expert is convinced that the product is safe and quotes the tests that have been performed to illustrate this point. The environmentalist is not convinced, citing other evidence to show the product is doubtful. Then the environmentalist asks the expert: 'Can you guarantee that there is no risk attached to this product?' The expert replies: 'There is no evidence that this product poses a risk and there is much evidence that it is safe. However, as a scientist, I cannot give an absolute guarantee that there is no risk.' In a public debate the expert has now lost the argument because the public wants a guarantee. The activist guarantees risk; the expert cannot guarantee safety.

Science can make pronouncements in its own sphere probably with greater confidence than most other disciplines can make in their spheres. But it is also the nature of science that there is no certainty. In science there are only degrees of probability. Scientific knowledge must remain revisable in the light of new evidence. For example, an astronomer cannot guarantee that the Sun will rise tomorrow. The Sun has risen every dawn since the formation of the Earth, and we know why from the laws of celestial mechanics. The probability that the Sun will rise tomorrow is enormously large and from a common-sense point of view the matter is certain. However, the probability that the Sun will fail to rise is not zero. It is computable and, from a scientific viewpoint, sunrise cannot be guaranteed.

Let me return to the expert and the activist. Let us assume that the expert is unbiased, that he or she has carried out extensive tests and has reviewed *all* the literature on the subject. Let us say that, as a result, the expert can have a confidence level of ninety-six per cent that the product is safe. This leaves a doubt of four per cent, mainly because product safety has not been tested under an absolutely enormous number of conditions. The activist's case that the product is dangerous has only a four per cent chance of being correct, but a ninety-six per cent chance of being incorrect.

Of course, I deliberately fabricated the preceding scene in order to make a particular point. However, my aim is not to canonise experts and to damn environmental activists. In some cases the expert is no more than a 'hired gun', recruited to put an acceptable face on self-interest, and in some cases the activists are experts who take every effort to base conclusions on objective data. Many other cases fall somewhere in between. But unfortunately the scene I painted, where the activist seems largely motivated by an evangelical faith, is not uncommon.

Life is a risky business. You cannot avoid risk even if you stay in bed. If you do, your muscles will waste from disuse and a plane may drop on the house from the sky and kill you. Things get really hairy when you get out of bed. There is a real danger you will trip and fall down the stairs. Next you must avoid electrocuting yourself as you cook breakfast. Then to the deadliest danger of all—driving to work. About five hundred people are killed on Irish roads every year and thousands are injured. And so it goes on through the day, everyday. Every living moment is accompanied by risk.

The only way to live, therefore, is to decide what activities are worth pursuing, try to understand and measure the risk involved, devise ways to avoid or minimise the risk and then proceed with caution. Sometimes our analysis will indicate that the risk so far outweighs the benefit that we should avoid the activity altogether—for example, unprotected sunbathing for fair-skinned people.

Demands are often made in the environmental area that we must not proceed in certain directions until we are certain that it is safe to do so. This sounds sensible, but we must remember that little or no human progress would ever have been made if this advice had always been followed. The only sensible way to do things is to proceed with caution as previously described. For example, in the 1950s, a strong argument was made against humans landing on the Moon lest they carry back an alien organism that might devastate life on earth. It was decided after much analysis to go ahead anyway, although returning astronauts from the first missions were quarantined for a period on earth to check them out. Going ahead with the Moon missions was the right decision, even though absolute guarantees could not be given in advance that the missions posed no risk. To cancel the missions based on the fears of a tiny theoretical risk would have dealt a massive blow to the human spirit. On the other hand, there is now sufficient evidence that the build-up of greenhouse gases is causing the world to heat up. It would therefore be irresponsible to continue to allow these gases to increase.

And finally, an example of the selective targeting of one risk while ignoring another. We all continually breathe in the natural radioactive gas radon which emanates from rocks in the earth. It is estimated that radon is responsible for ten per cent of lung cancers, but public consciousness of the problem is very low. In some parts of Ireland indoor radon builds up to unacceptable levels in domestic houses. One example is a 10 km square in the south-eastern part of Cork city and its surrounds, including part of the harbour. A few years ago I described this in a newspaper article and pointed out that it is relatively easy and inexpensive to reduce high radon levels. I received a telephone call from an environmental activist who asked me to identify the industries in Cork harbour that emit radon. I explained that radon was not coming from industry but from the earth. The activist immediately dropped interest in radon since it is not an industrial hazard.

Do Synthetic Chemicals in our Environment Threaten our Future?

A recent controversial look at the health effects of environmental chemical pollution attracted much attention. This was the book *Our Stolen Future* by Theo Colburn, J. P. Myers and D. Dumanoski (Little Brown and Co., 1996). The authors argue that the world is everywhere polluted with persistent chemicals that mimic human hormones and that have insidious and serious effects, mainly on the human reproduction system. For example, recent studies report that male sperm counts have declined by fifty per cent over the last fifty years. In other words, the future of the human species may be compromised. However, the evidence, although indicative, falls well short of proving the case and the authors admit this. Nevertheless, the argument is strong enough to merit serious investigation.

Hormones are natural chemicals in the body that regulate growth, body chemistry, reproduction and the functioning of various organs. They are secreted in minute concentrations (parts per million) into the bloodstream by various glands and they travel to their tissue destinations where they exert their effects.

For example, the thyroid gland in the neck secretes a hormone called thyroxine, which regulates our general rate of body metabolism and also has a profound effect on the rate of development from the infantile into the adult form. The main male sex hormone is testosterone (produced in the testes) and the main female sex hormone is oestradiol (produced in the ovaries). Both are important in controlling sexual development and characteristics. A deficiency or excess of any of the hormones upsets the chemical equilibrium of the body and can play havoc with normal development and with general health.

Since 1940 the world has seen an explosion of synthetic chemical use in plastics, herbicides, insecticides, wood preservatives, paints, etc. In 1992, eight hundred billion kilograms of carbon-based synthetic chemicals were manufactured globally. There are about 100,000 synthetic chemicals on the market and 1,000 new ones are introduced each year. Five kilograms of pesticides are used per capita per year in the USA.

Before a synthetic chemical is released onto the public market it is tested for possible effects on human health. Prior to the 1940s, these tests concentrated on acute poisonous effects—does exposure to the chemical make you ill or kill you? Since the 1940s, the safety tests have concentrated almost exclusively on the potential of chemicals to cause cancer in those exposed to them and birth defects in babies born to exposed mothers. This is fine as far as it goes but, according to this book, it doesn't go far enough. The authors claim that many synthetic chemicals mimic natural hormone action and can therefore interfere with normal hormonal regulation of the body. New synthetic chemicals are not checked for this effect.

The authors describe the work of biologist Frederick von Saal to illustrate the exquisite sensitivity of living organisms, especially during development, even to the tiniest variation in natural hormone levels. Von Saal correlated the adult behaviour and characteristics of individual male and female mice, from the same litter, with the physical location they had in the mother's womb. About one in six female mice are carried in the womb sandwiched between two brothers. These females are thus exposed to more male testosterone during development than sisters who lie between sisters, but only about one part per billion more. Von Saal noted that such females as adults behaved more aggressively than their sisters, came into puberty later, had less heat and were less attractive to males. Similarly, males carried in the womb between females developed differently from males carried between males.

Problems associated with ingestion of synthetic chemicals that have actions that mimic hormones are well illustrated by the diethylstilbesterol (DES) story. DES acts like oestrogen (a female sex hormone) and was synthesised in the laboratory in 1938. It was administered to women in a widespread fashion, mainly to treat problems in pregnancy. No birth defects were noticed following its use and, anyway, it was believed that chemicals ingested by the mother did not cross the placental barrier to the foetus. However, years later, problems were noticed during the development of children of mothers who had taken DES. Girls were more prone to develop vaginal cancer. It was also reported that boys had reproductive problems, such as abnormal sperm and undescended testicles, but the evidence was not conclusive here.

The experience with DES showed that the body can mistake a synthetic chemical for a hormone. The insecticide DDT also mimics female sex hormones when ingested. Of fifty-one synthetic chemicals that are loose in the environment and that are known hormone disrupters, over half are long-lived, i.e. do not readily break down to harmless chemicals in the environment. One of the best known is a family called the polychlorinated biphenyls (PCBs). These were synthesised in 1929 and put into widespread use as coolants in the electrical industry and as additives to plastics. Their production was banned in most western countries in the 1970s. However, prior and subsequent to that, spillages and leaks released them into the environment and, being long-lived, they remain in the food chain.

Other known hormone disrupters are nonylphenol, dioxins and phthalates. Nonylphenol is added to polystyrene and plastics to make them stable and pliable. Industrial detergents also contain chemicals that can break down to nonylphenol. Nonylphenol can leach in low concentrations from plastics and has been shown to be an oestrogen mimic. Dioxin is another long-lasting chemical that is generated by burning certain plastics and fossil fuels. Phthalates are used in plastics, paints, inks and adhesives. In 1996, BBC Radio reported that leading brands of baby milk powder were contaminated with levels of phthalate that have been shown in animal experiments to interfere with male sexual development

We have been ingesting these chemicals from the food chain at low levels for a long time. According to the authors, most people's blood contains PCBs, DDT and dioxins at a concentration of parts per billion or parts per trillion. Are such levels sufficiently high to affect the developing foetus in the mothers womb? Also, many of these chemicals concentrate in body fat and the authors claim that they are secreted in a more concentrated form in mothers' milk. Will nursing mothers pass on a problem to the infant? Experiments with animals indicate that feeding very low levels of some of these chemicals to pregnant rats at a critical stage can produce offspring with damaged reproduction systems. The big question in the book is: have we compromised the reproductive future of our children?

These chemicals have been in the environment for fifty years. If they have any effect one would predict that it would be transgenerational and mainly affect sexual reproductive function. Is there any evidence for such effects? The authors cite various studies to illustrate that such evidence does exist. Three studies have shown a decline in sperm counts by up to fifty per cent over the last fifty years. Testicular cancer rates have increased (e.g. a three-fold increase in Denmark) over the same period, and there are reports of increased rates of undescended testicles in England and Wales for the period 1962–82. In women, rates of ectopic pregnancies have increased. Also since 1940, rates of breast cancer have increased by one per cent per year. As a general principle, risk of breast cancer is linked to lifelong exposure to oestrogen.

So what do we make of all this? First of all, there is no need to panic. The evidence in this matter is far from conclusive. This is clear from the book, even though the authors naturally have a vested interest in making their case as plausible as possible. I therefore conclude that the real strength of the case is considerably less than it seems. For example, studies that fail to find a link between naturally occurring levels of hormone mimicking chemicals and health effects are not emphasised. Also, demonstrating an effect in an experimental animal does not necessarily mean that the same thing applies in humans. The human sperm count data are worrying but other studies have found no decline in sperm counts.

However, the evidence is sufficiently strong to take serious notice. From now on synthetic chemicals should be tested for their hormone mimicking capacity. Intensive study should be carried out to further test the hypothesis put forward in this book. If the hypothesis holds up, serious measures would be justified such as strictly controlling female diet until the time of the menopause. In the meantime, the extra stress caused by worrying about the matter in the absence of firmer evidence could well cause more harm than any effects the chemicals might have.

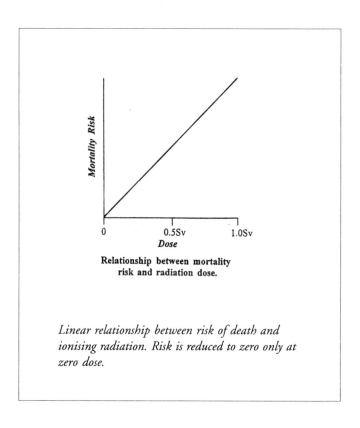

Relationship between mortality
risk and radiation dose.

*Linear relationship between risk of death and
ionising radiation. Risk is reduced to zero only at
zero dose.*

How Dangerous is Ionising Radiation?

Radiation is a general term and covers many different forms of radiation, including visible light, ultraviolet light, microwaves, radio waves and X-rays. Radiation can be divided into two broad categories—ionising radiation and non-ionising radiation. Ionising radiation is the particular type of radiation emitted by radioactive substances. It differs from non-ionising radiation in that it is very energetic and has the capacity to ionise matter when it interacts with it.

Matter is composed of atoms. The atoms are normally electrically neutral, i.e. positive and negative charges are balanced. Ionising radiation can strip negatively charged electrons off atoms to produce positively charged atoms and the process is called ionisation. It is disruptive of the orderly structure of matter. If the matter is biological body tissue, there is a risk that the damage will initiate the development of a cancer or, if the damaged tissue is in the germ line (i.e. leading to the production of sperm in males or eggs in females), result in a genetic defect in a future generation.

Broadly speaking, the general public is exposed to ionising radiation from two sources—natural and artificial. The world is naturally radioactive and always has been. The main form of artificial radiation is medical ionising radiation (principally diagnostic X-rays). Other forms of artificial radiation include emissions from nuclear industry, fallout from nuclear weapons tests and stray radiation from miscellaneous appliances (e.g. televisions).

Under normal circumstances the great majority of the ionising radiation we receive comes from natural sources, mostly from the radioactive gas radon. Most of the artificial ionising radiation that we receive comes from medicine. Generally we receive very little radiation from the nuclear industry, nuclear fallout and miscellaneous appliances.

Natural ionising radiation is composed of cosmic radiation, internal radiation and terrestrial radiation. Cosmic radiation showers down onto the earth from outer space. Our bodies are naturally radioactive because the earth is radioactive and this radioactivity gets into our food and hence enters our bodies. We are also irradiated externally by rocks on the Earth's surface. The largest component of our exposure to natural ionising radiation is the radioactive gas radon which escapes into the air from rocks in the Earth. There is little or nothing we can do to protect ourselves from cosmic, internal or external radiation from rocks, but luckily we can take steps to minimise our exposure to radon (see chapter starting on p. 189).

When ionising radiation interacts with biological tissue, it deposits energy there. The amount of energy deposited per unit mass of tissue is called the absorbed dose and the size of this dose determines the probability that a harmful health effect will ensue. The unit of dose is called the Sievert (Sv). One thousandth of a Sv is a millisievert (mSv). When calculating overall doses of radiation to the population (collective dose), you multiply the average individual dose by the total number of exposed people. Collective dose is expressed as man-sieverts or man-millisieverts. The average individual annual dose in Ireland from ionising radiation is about 3 mSv. Of the annual collective dose received by the Irish population approximately 86.9 per cent comes from natural radiation, 12.6 per cent from medical radiation, 0.03 per cent from nuclear discharges, 0.17 per cent from nuclear fallout and 0.4 per cent from miscellaneous sources.

It is very important to understand the risk from ionising radiation in order to decide how to take sensible protective precautions. Ill effects resulting from exposure to radiation are divided into early and late effects. Early effects are associated only with the accumulation of large doses of radiation (greater than 1 Sv) over a short period (hours or days). These effects include radiation sickness (diarrhoea, vomiting) and possible death within days or weeks. The radiation dose that is lethal within thirty days for fifty per cent of those exposed to it is about 3 Grays (at these high acute doses, the term Gray is used instead of Sievert). An acute dose of 8 Grays or more will almost certainly result in early death; an acute dose of 1.5 Grays or less will very probably not.

These high doses could only be received as a result of a nuclear war or being close to a nuclear accident. A more practical and important matter is to know the risks associated with low doses of radiation (in the mSv range) accumulated over long periods—the sort of doses that we receive in our everyday lives. These doses carry a risk of long-term effects, such as cancer and hereditary defects. With cancer there is a long latent period between the initial biological damage from the radiation and the subsequent clinical manifestation of the tumour. This can range from a few years to forty years, or longer. Hereditary effects, of course, cannot be expressed until the next generation at the earliest.

For late cancer effects, the relationship between risk of fatal cancer and dose is known reasonably accurately for larger doses (that is, significant fractions of a Sievert and upwards). It is known with much less precision for lower doses. The main reason for this is that at low doses the effects are small and therefore difficult to detect with statistical validity. If the effects were large there would be no difficulty in detecting and quantifying them.

Consider the difficulties. Because the effects are small you must study a large population exposed to a low level of radiation. You must have a similarly large population of controls against which you will compare your test group. The two groups must be similar to each other in every way, except that the test group received a defined amount of dose extra to the controls. You must know accurately how much extra radiation the test group received. You must carefully monitor the groups for clinical symptoms over a period of fifty and more years, because of the latency phenomenon in cancer. It is easy to see that such a study would be very difficult.

The current general scientific consensus on the form of the relationship between risk (of fatal cancer) and dose (for lower doses over protracted time) is the linear no threshold model—risk is directly proportional to dose all the way down to zero dose. Risk is reduced to zero only at zero dose and there is no low threshold of dose below which there is no risk. This is the basis for the statement often heard: 'there is no safe level of radiation'. This statement is frequently misunderstood as meaning that radiation is equally dangerous regardless of the dose. The truth is that a tiny dose carries a tiny risk, a medium dose carries a medium risk, a large dose carries a large risk. The popular saying would be more accurately phrased: 'there is no absolutely safe level of radiation'. Another consequence of the linear model is that a given collective dose has the same health consequences, no matter how it is distributed. For example, 1,000 people each receiving 1 mSv will have the same consequences as 100 people each receiving 10 mSv.

The single most useful body of data used to determine the risk of ionising radiation is the Japanese study of the survivors of the atomic bombings at Hiroshima and Nagasaki in 1945. Other useful data has come from long term follow-up studies of patients who received defined doses of radiation in therapeutic medicine, for example in the treatment of ringworm.

Two major international committees continually evaluate the radiation risk data. These are the International Committee on Radiological Protection (ICRP) and the United Nations Sub-Committee on Atomic Radiation (UNSCEAR) and they issue their findings and recommendations. These bodies have come up with a nominal mortality risk of five per cent per Sv for fatal cancer from irradiation at low doses for a population of all ages. In other words, if one million people, of all ages, each receive 1 mSv of ionising radiation this will result in fifty fatal cancers attributable to exposure to the radiation. One million people each receiving 1 mSv will also result in the expression of six serious hereditary defects in their descendants over all future generations.

Ionising Radiation and the Atomic Bomb

I was looking through a popular junior science primer recently. It is generally a clearly written exposition of the basic principles of physics, chemistry and biology. Various general remarks are made in the introductory chapter, such as on the sources of energy used by society. In the few paragraphs devoted to nuclear energy, my eye was caught by a description of the health effects of the ionising radiation released when the atomic bomb (A-bomb) was exploded over Nagasaki in 1945. The description echoes a widely held, exaggerated view of the effects of the radiation released in the explosion.

Specifically, the authors state that the radiation released in the bombing killed 25,000 people and, subsequently, numerous genetic defects were noted resulting from exposure to the radiation. The truth of the matter is that the effects of the radiation alone were not as severe as this and, so far, the Japanese A-bomb data provide no evidence of genetic damage.

Let me say right away that I have no intention of trying to minimise the consequences of the use of the first atomic weapons on Japan. I believe that science betrayed itself in developing the atomic bomb and that the first use of the bombs was a turning point, not only in warfare, but in human history. I also accept that in both cases, that is in its development and use, powerful mitigating circumstances and arguments applied. But that is a story for another day.

The medical data on the survivors of the atomic explosions in Japan provide the single most important study on which estimates of the health effects of human exposure to ionising radiation are based. Scientifically, the data are very good and results based on their analysis are used in setting standards to ensure protection of workers and the general public from harmful effects arising from useful applications of ionising radiation, such as in medicine.

Two A-bombs were exploded in Japan at the end of the Second World War. The first was exploded over the city of Hiroshima on 6 August, 1945, and the second over the city of Nagasaki three days later. Although small in comparison to the nuclear weapons now available, the explosive power of the first A-bombs was immensely greater than conventional bombs. The explosive power of the Hiroshima bomb was equivalent to about 15,000 tons of TNT, and that of the Nagasaki bomb to about 25,000 tons.

Atomic bombs differ from conventional weapons in that their explosion releases large amounts of radioactive elements and ionising radiation in addition to the tremendous heat and blast energies.

Hiroshima had a civilian population of 250,000. On the day of the explosion, 45,000 people died and a further 19,000 died within the next four months. Nagasaki had a population of 174,000. On the day of the explosion 22,000 people died and 17,000 more during the next four months. These are recorded civilian deaths. Unrecorded deaths of military personnel and foreign workers may have added significantly to these figures.

It is impossible to estimate the proportion of these 103,000 deaths that were caused by radiation alone, rather than by the extremely high temperatures and blast pressure caused by the explosions. It is known that the radiation effects alone would have been sufficient to kill a majority of those exposed within a kilometre of ground zero (i.e. the point below which the bombs exploded) within days or weeks. However, most of those who died in this area would have been killed more or less instantly from the effects of blast, fire and falling buildings. In other words, they died in ways indistinguishable from the countless people who died in conventional bombing attacks on Cologne, Essen or London. Actually, the loss of life in the A-bomb explosions was considerably less than from the fire-raids on Tokyo a few months before, or on Dresden the previous year, when 130,000 people died in the fire-bombing.

A commission was established immediately after the end of the war in order to study the long-term effects of exposure to the atomic radiation on the health of the survivors. This work continues to this day and is called the Life Span Study (LSS). The two major, long-term health effects that may result from exposure to ionising radiation are (a) cancer, and (b) transmission of a hereditary defect to the next and/or later generations. Excess cancers have been noted amongst the survivors of the A-bomb explosions. However, it is too early yet to get significant results on genetic effects (if there are any).

A total of 86,572 people who survived the atomic explosions have been followed up in the LSS study. Of these, 52,200 received significant doses of radiation—average dose 260 mSv. (We each receive an annual dose of about 3 mSv in Ireland, mostly from natural radiation.) The first type of cancer to emerge after exposure to radiation is leukaemia—cancer of the blood. Amongst the 52,200 significantly exposed survivors, 176 died from leukaemia between 1950 and 1990, and 86 (49 per cent) of these are attributable to radiation exposure. Solid cancers show up after the leukaemias. In the significantly exposed group, there were 4,687 deaths from solid cancers between 1950 and 1990. Of these, 341 are attributable to radiation (7 per cent). Of the 4,863 total cancer deaths in this significantly exposed group, 427 (9 per cent) are attributable to radiation exposure. In other words, the other 91 per cent of cancer deaths would have occurred even if no atomic bomb explosions had occurred.

Essentially everything we know about hereditary defects induced by radiation comes from laboratory experiments with animals. The largest group of humans available for such a study are the Japanese survivors of the A-bomb explosions. However, in order to get statistically meaningful data in the study of transmission of hereditary defects, very large numbers of subjects are necessary, and the Japanese cohort is rather small by these standards. Also, insufficient time has passed since exposure to the radiation. Several generations must elapse before the full extent of any effects would be expected to show up. At the present time there is no evidence of any genetic changes in the children born to the Japanese survivors.

The twentieth century has produced many powerful symbols by which it will be remembered. An example of a good symbol is the image of Neil Armstrong standing on the Moon. Two examples of bad symbols are the swastika and the huge mushroom cloud rising into the sky. I believe the latter is the worst of all.

The mushroom symbol has deeply scarred the human psyche for over fifty years. It signifies our monstrous creation—the ability to destroy civilisation. Throughout the long Cold War, we all suffered in blank despair under this horrible spectre. And then, suddenly, it faded to a pale shadow of its former horror with the collapse of the Soviet empire. What I can't understand now is why the West is apparently content to sit back and watch Russia wallow in economic chaos. Why are we not pumping in massive assistance in order to help them to achieve stable political conditions and an efficient free market economy? The last thing we want to risk is history repeating itself and another mushroom cloud rearing up its horrible head again.

Radon, the Silent Natural Menace

Radon is a natural radioactive gas that escapes into the atmosphere from rocks in the earth. When we breathe, the radioactivity enters our lungs and can lodge there, irradiating the tissue at close quarters. This irradiation carries a low level risk of causing lung cancer. In some houses radon levels can build up to an extent that carries an unacceptable risk. It is a straightforward matter to measure the radon level in your home and, if it is unacceptably high, you can take steps to lower the level without incurring too much expense.

Radon is present everywhere in the air. It is no more possible to completely avoid breathing radon than it is to avoid breathing air. Radon contributes over fifty per cent of the total radiation dose received by the Irish public every year. It is, therefore, easily the single biggest source of exposure to radiation encountered by the public. (The average Irish person receives at least 1,500 times more radiation from radon each year than he or she receives from Sellafield.) On the other hand, radon is the only form of natural radiation over which we have any control and we certainly can take steps to ensure that we do not breathe excessive amounts of radon indoors.

Uranium is a radioactive element naturally present in rocks. Rocks of igneous origin, such as granite, have greater amounts of uranium than sedimentary rocks, such as limestone. Uranium breaks down into radioactive daughter products, one of which is the gas radon. Radon levels are expressed in terms of becquerels per cubic meter (Bq/m^3). The gas escapes from rocks into the air where it is massively diluted to low background level—4 to 10 Bq/m^3.

Radon enters our houses mainly from the soil underneath the foundations. Small amounts can enter the house from the construction materials in the house itself and some can also be carried in by the water

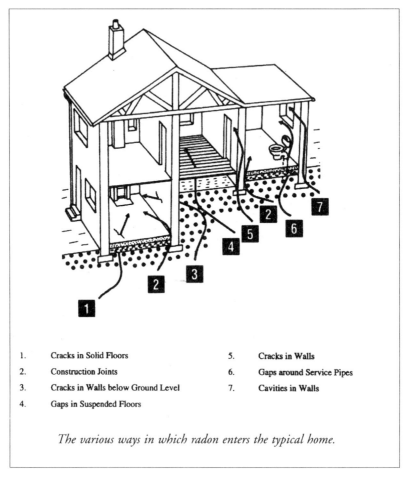

1.	Cracks in Solid Floors	5.	Cracks in Walls
2.	Construction Joints	6.	Gaps around Service Pipes
3.	Cracks in Walls below Ground Level	7.	Cavities in Walls
4.	Gaps in Suspended Floors		

The various ways in which radon enters the typical home.

supply. Having entered the house, radon does not find it easy to escape back to the outside because of restricted ventilation. Restriction of ventilation is exacerbated in the modern home. Measures such as double glazing, draughtproofing and attic insulation are effective in reducing heat loss but they also reduce ventilation rates. In such a modern house, there is a greater probability that radon will reach high levels than in the old draughty house, with windows that rattle and a fireplace in every bedroom.

In the mid-1980s a nation-wide study of indoor radon, carried out by Dr Jim McLaughlin of University College, Dublin (UCD), found that the average indoor radon concentration in Ireland was 60 Bq/m³ and that four per cent of housing stock had radon levels that exceeded 200 Bq/m^3. An indoor radon level of 200 Bq/m^3 has been adopted by the government as a reference level—that is, a level at or above which remedial action is recommended to reduce radon levels. The average lifetime risk of contracting lung cancer in Ireland is three per cent. An indoor radon level of 200 Bq/m^3 almost doubles this risk. This is considered to be unacceptable in view of the fact that effective measures for radon remediation are available.

The UCD survey showed the highest levels of radon in the west of Ireland, principally in Galway and in parts of Mayo. High levels were also found in Cork City and in parts of Clare. In 1989, the Radiological Protection Institute of Ireland (RPII) began a programme of detailed radon surveys. The first surveys were carried out in areas shown by the UCD study to have high radon levels. The first detailed survey was carried out in the west and in 1991 a detailed survey was carried out in Cork City. The RPII continued from there to carry out radon surveys around the entire country, a project which is now essentially completed. Some of the results give cause for concern.

The RPII has estimated the percentage of housing stock that exceeds the reference radon level in each 10 km square of the country. Calculations have been made for 837 such squares and in ninety-eight of these squares (12 per cent) over twenty per cent of housing stock is estimated to exceed the reference radon level. Generally, higher indoor radon levels have been noted in counties Galway, Mayo, Clare, Sligo, Wicklow, Carlow, Kilkenny and Wexford. For example, thirty per cent of houses surveyed across Galway City have radon levels that exceed the reference value. In Cork, between ten and twenty per cent of the housing stock in a 10 km square in the south-eastern part of the city and suburbs has radon levels greater than the reference level.

It is certainly advisable to have your home checked for radon levels. You can do this by applying to the Radiological Protection Institute of Ireland, 3 Clonskeagh Square, Clonskeagh Road, Dublin 14 (Tel. No. 01 269 7766). The RPII also operates a Radon Free Phone (1 800 300600). If the radon measurement results indicate that you have high radon levels, you can get advice on radon remediation from the

Department of the Environment. You can also get information on both radioactivity and radon by writing to ENFO, 17 St Andrew Street, Dublin 2 and asking for briefing sheet number 15 on radon and number 7 on radioactivity.

It is more complicated to reduce radon levels in an existing house than it is to build in radon protection as a new house is being constructed. In the latter case it is a straightforward matter, involving the positioning of sumps under the foundation and venting these to the outside through PVC pipes. Also, a continuous thick plastic sheeting is laid down to prevent radon from getting into the house. This work costs several hundred pounds. It costs several times more than this to treat a radon problem in an existing house.

The building regulations in Ireland now require that all new houses under construction in high radon areas must be fitted with inbuilt protection against radon. This involves installing sumps and plastic barriers. A high radon area is an area in which the probability is ten per cent or more that an untreated house will exceed the radon reference level. New houses under construction in areas not classified as high radon areas must have sumps fitted.

Finally, studies indicate that smokers are more susceptible to radon than non-smokers—another reason to stop the habit if you are a smoker.

Radiation from Electric Power is Not a Significant Cause of Cancer

There is much current debate about the potential of the electromagnetic radiation associated with electric power to cause ill-health, particularly cancer. A study published by J. D. Jackson in the April 1992 edition of the 'Proceedings of the National Academy of Sciences', USA, clearly demonstrates that, amongst the population at large, such radiation is not a significant cause of cancer.

On the other hand, there is some evidence that particular groups exposed to increased levels of this form of electromagnetic radiation are at increased risk of developing cancer. For example, there is evidence of a weak association between increased exposure and an increased risk of leukaemia in children. There is also evidence of an increased carcinogenic risk in workers whose occupations have a higher exposure to magnetic fields. However, both in the case of children and exposed workers, contradictory studies have been published and much more research is needed before we can say anything for sure in these areas.

We are all pretty much continually exposed to electromagnetic radiation fields that stray from the ubiquitous circuitry of electric power that exists in our environment. Electric power is generated in a power station and is transmitted over long distances in high-voltage cables that run high over the ground. The power is thus directed to numerous substations from whence it is redirected at lower voltage to transformers for local distribution. The transformer steps the power down to a voltage of 220/240 volts for domestic consumption. Typically, local power distribution is carried along the streets on cables mounted twenty to thirty feet above the ground. Finally, within our houses the power is carried through conduits in the walls to outlets for lights, equipment and appliances.

The mechanism for the transmission and distribution of electric power has remained essentially unchanged since the 1920s. However, the volume of power generation and the volume of domestic consumption of electricity has increased dramatically since then. It follows, therefore, that the exposure of the general population to the electromagnetic radiation that strays from electric power has increased throughout the century directly in step with the increase in power generation and domestic consumption. If electromagnetic radiation is a significant factor in inducing cancer, one would expect this to be reflected in the pattern of cancer statistics recorded over the same period. Jackson's 1992 study compared cancer statistics, volume of power generation and per capita residential power consumption in the USA over the period 1900 to the present.

The illustration plots per capita electric power generation, per capita electric power consumption, mortality rate from all cancers, mortality rate from respiratory cancers and mortality rate from all cancers except respiratory cancers, for the period 1900–1990 in the USA. Power generation and power consumption increased exponentially over this period. Per capita electric power generation increased by a factor of more than 300 between 1902 and 1990. In the past fifty years it has increased by a factor of more than ten. Similar increases have occurred in per capita residential consumption, with an increase by a factor of twenty in the past fifty years. The exposure of the population to unavoidable low intensity stray electromagnetic fields has also increased by roughly the same factors over the same time period.

The illustration also shows the age-adjusted death rates from all cancers. This rate has increased relatively little, from 0.8 deaths per 1,000 per year in 1900 to 1.3 deaths per 1,000 per year in 1970. It has been essentially constant since then. Some of the increase in the early years is certainly attributable to more complete reporting of the cause of death.

The illustration also shows that respiratory cancer mortality has been steadily increasing since 1930. When respiratory cancer mortality is subtracted from the total cancer mortality data, we see that, since 1940, the death rate

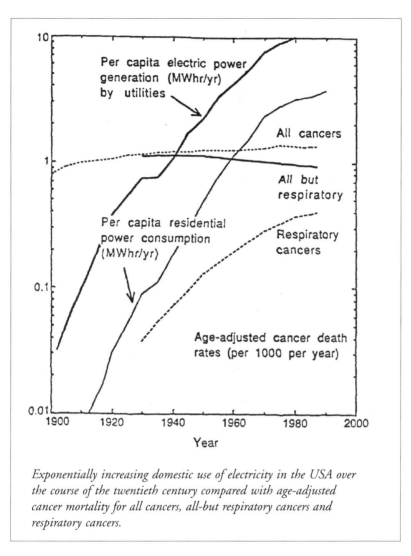

Exponentially increasing domestic use of electricity in the USA over the course of the twentieth century compared with age-adjusted cancer mortality for all cancers, all-but respiratory cancers and respiratory cancers.

from all other cancers has been slowly declining. The great bulk of respiratory cancers are caused by cigarette smoking. The remaining minor increases and decreases in all other cancer mortality rates have occurred in a general background of extremely rapid growth in the generation and use of electric power by society. This data shows that the stray radiation associated with the generation, distribution and use of electricity is not a significant cause of overall cancer deaths in the population.

However, an alternative explanation for the data shown in the figure might be that increased exposure to the electromagnetic fields does indeed cause an increase in the incidence of cancer but that this effect is not apparent in cancer mortality data because of the improved cure rates achieved by modern medicine. This explanation does not hold water. Medical intervention in cancer has been a qualified failure as regards significantly affecting overall cancer mortality rates.

Reliable US data on age-adjusted incidence rates for various cancers exist from 1969 to 1986 and are cited in Jackson's paper. I will consider data for all cancers, lung and bronchial cancers, leukaemia and childhood leukaemia. There was a seventeen per cent increase in total incidence rates from 1969–1986, a thirty-five per cent rise in respiratory cancers and a slight decrease in the overall incidence of leukaemia. The incidence rate of childhood leukaemia was essentially constant over this period. Also over this same period generation and consumption of electric power per capita increased by a factor of two, which is much greater than the cancer incidence increase. Furthermore, most of the slow increase in rate of 0.93 per cent per year over the period 1969–1986 is largely caused by increases in the cancer rates for four sites—lung and bronchus, colon and rectum, breast and prostate. Cancers of the four sites mentioned each have established or inferred causes that do not include stray electromagnetic fields. Therefore, at most only a very small fraction of the 0.93 per cent per year increase in total incidence rate could conceivably be attributed to electromagnetic fields. Leukaemia, in particular, shows no sign of increasing incidence for the period 1950 to the present.

Jackson concludes from his study that:

n There cannot be any significant overall cause of cancer from the use of electricity in society.

n There is no evidence that stray electromagnetic fields cause leukaemia.

Therefore, the average person need not be worried about using electrical appliances or walking beneath overhead power lines. However, Jackson's data does not rule out possible risks to very small segments of the population particularly susceptible to this radiation for one reason or another.

Health Risks from Microwave Radiation

Microwave radiation is widely used in communications and other technological devices. There is considerable ongoing debate about its possible health effects. In this chapter I will deal with microwave radiation use in mobile phones, multi-point microwave distribution systems (MMDS) and microwave ovens.

Microwave radiation is part of a family of radiations called the electromagnetic spectrum. The other members of this spectrum include cosmic, gamma and ultraviolet radiations, visible light, infrared radiation, radio waves and extremely low frequency radiation (associated with electricity). These radiations travel through space as waves and at the speed of light. A wave can be identified by its wavelength (distance from peak to peak) and by its frequency (the number of peaks that pass a stationary point every second). High frequency radiation has a small wavelength and low frequency radiation has a long wavelength.

Frequency is measured in cycles per second. One cycle per second is one hertz (Hz). One million cycles per second is a megahertz (MHz) and one thousand million cycles per second is a gigahertz (GHz). Microwave radiations range in frequency from 300 MHz to 300 GHz, and from 1 metre to 1 millimetre in wavelength.

Everyone who has a microwave oven knows that microwaves can heat biological tissue. Microwaves also have other subtle (athermal) effects, but the heating effect is the best understood. Excessive heating of any part of the body is undesirable and limits of exposure to microwaves are set in order to prevent overheating. Parts of the body that are poorly supplied with a cooling blood supply are particularly at risk, for example the lens of the eye. The International Radiation Protection Association (IRPA) recommends exposure limits that are widely followed by national regulatory agencies.

197

Exposure limits are stated as the intensity of the radiation field (power density) above which one should not be exposed. Power density is expressed as milliwatts per square centimetre (mW/cm^2). A milliwatt (mW) is one thousandth of a watt, a microwatt (μW) is one millionth of a watt, and a nanowatt (nW) is one thousand millionth of a watt.

The frequency of microwave radiation used to carry information between mobile phones and transmission towers (high masts spaced about fifteen miles apart) is 900 MHz. The power density limit for this frequency is 1 mW/cm^2. The microwave transmission is made at relatively low power—about 300 watts. The typical power density at the base of a transmission mast would be much less than 0.02 mW/cm^2—well below the IRPA limit of 1 mW/cm^2. However, power density of microwave radiation around the antennae of many mobile phone hand sets has been quoted at around 0.45 mW/cm^2, which is close to the IRPA limit for the general public.

Most public concern about mobile phones relates to the transmission masts. However, if there are health effects, they are more likely to be associated with the hand sets. People fear the unfamiliar. Transmission masts look menacing and alien. The mobile hand set is just a familiar telephone. To be on the safe side, when making or receiving a mobile phone call, make sure that the antenna is at least 2.5 cm from your head. Proprietary carrying pouches can now be purchased that significantly reduce the microwave radiation coming from the mobile phone antenna. Your inner ear might be at risk from heating because it has a poor cooling blood supply. Obviously, the shorter you keep your mobile phone calls, the less microwave radiation you receive.

Public concern with MMDS centres on the locations of the towers that transmit the 2.66 GHz microwave TV signal. Measurements show that the microwave power density on the ground around these towers is very low and typical power densities (1nW/cm^2) in the closest houses are one million times below the IRPA limit.

The microwave oven cooks food using 2.45 GHz microwaves and works well with foods that have a liquid water content. The microwave radiation penetrates about three centimetres into the food and vibrates water molecules at the microwave frequency. This sets up a friction, producing heat, just as you can warm your hands by briskly rubbing them together. When you switch on the microwave oven, heating immediately begins within the bulk of the food, which is why the effect is so fast.

In the electric oven, the electric elements must first warm the air which then warms the food from the outside in. This is a much slower process. The fact that microwave cooking depends on liquid water can be illustrated as follows. Take a well frozen, dry (pat it lightly with paper towels to ensure this) piece of ice. Place it in the microwave oven and switch it on. The ice will not melt.

Microwave ovens are designed to be safe. An interlock instantly shuts off the microwaves if the oven door is opened while the machine is on. Ovens are designed to ensure that power density due to microwave leakage should not exceed 2.5 mW/cm^2 at any point beyond 2.5 cm from the external casing. There have been reports of higher readings and of microwave leaks around door seals. It is important to keep this part of the oven clean and well maintained. It is also best to walk away from the microwave oven when it is in operation. Even if the oven is leaking, the power density of the radiation drops off rapidly with distance from the oven.

Much research has been carried out into possible athermal effects of microwave radiation on health. Results of studies to date allow few precise conclusions to be drawn, but it would seem fair to conclude that, if there are health effects, they are small. However, prior to this century, humanity was not exposed to these artificial microwave, radio-frequency and extremely low frequency radiations. People are right to be wary. We should take prudent steps to limit avoidable exposure to these radiations.

A Green Future with Technology

The environmental movement has been a most important twentieth century development. It has drawn widespread public attention to the pressures and damage inflicted on natural world systems by the unrelenting march of modern technology. But, unfortunately, much of the environmental movement allowed itself to become frozen into a technophobic attitude that at once fixes modern technology with a baleful stare, while looking backwards at pre-industrial societies through a misty sentimental lens that only produces benign images. Thankfully this is changing. The Green movement is beginning to recognise that the technological revolution is irreversible and also that technology can, and must, be used to produce a healthy environment.

The capacity for goodness, decency and generosity—qualities essential for progress—and the capacity for bad behaviour and selfishness, that impedes progress, are embedded in our fundamental human nature and this has not changed much over the ages. The pre-industrial past was not one long saga of environmental wisdom as many Greens like to believe. Primitive societies changed their environments in many ways through agriculture, domesticating animals, building, migrating, etc. In some cases they over-hunted and burned and used up forests.

People in past ages may not have been much more intrinsically motivated than ourselves to care for the environment. However, world population was small, technology was primitive and there was no capacity to interfere with natural systems on a global scale. Today's teeming populations and powerful technologies have utterly changed this picture. Everywhere we look now in the environment there is evidence of change brought about by human activities. The atmosphere, oceans and climate have been changed. Human activities alter the biosphere and affect the evolution of life everywhere. Species of animals and plants are disappearing and new ones are arising out of selective breeding.

There is virtually no chance that we will ever return to a situation of nature undisturbed by human activities—not that there ever was such a time. In other words, the option of repairing existing damage and then leaving nature alone really doesn't exist. Human society has reached the stage where it must assume responsibility for the world. Much of the damage we have created through the use of technology can be detected, monitored and repaired only by the application of more technology. The future lies in the understanding and scientific management of ecosystems in a healthy and sustainable manner.

A great number of the processes and products we use today are unsustainable. Many technologies were developed with little priority given to efficiency and they have prodigious appetites for resources. Other technologies are unsustainable because of the legacy they leave to the future, for example nuclear waste from the nuclear industry. The new genetic engineering technology offers great promise in many areas but could also cause huge problems if misused.

In order to achieve sustainable development we must phase out the use of fossil fuels, reduce consumption of energy and raw materials, use closed production cycles as much as possible and develop energy efficient transport. We can only achieve this by developing new technology. The windmill and the solar panel are two well-known examples that show this approach works.

The most mature end of the environmental movement already appreciates that the future lies in using technology rather than in demonising it. Greenpeace has shown commendable initiative in this area and has developed several technological products aimed at replacing conventional ones that cause damage. For example, prime culprits in the depletion of the Earth's ozone layer are the chlorofluorocarbons (CFCs), widely used in refrigeration. Greenpeace has developed a commercially viable domestic refrigerator (the Greenfreeze) that operates without using CFCs. Another major environmental problem is the enhancement of the greenhouse effect, to which the inefficient burning of fuel in motor cars contributes significantly. Greenpeace, in collaboration with Swiss engineers, has developed a highly fuel efficient

SmILE motor car. SmILE is so named because it stands for <u>Sm</u>all, <u>I</u>ntelligent, <u>L</u>ight and <u>E</u>fficient.

There are many other technological developments currently underway that promise great advantages for the environment. The Germans have developed a process for making 'biodiesel' from the rapeseed plant. Chemically, it is a methyl-ester and it gives the same engine performance and miles per gallon as conventional petroleum-based diesel. The good news is that the production and burning of biodiesel emits less than one quarter the volume of greenhouse gases as emitted by conventional diesel. Also, biodiesel has the great added advantage of being a renewable resource.

Another very promising technological development in France is the zero pollution car. The engine runs on compressed air which is carried in tanks like those used by scuba divers. The Mexican government is so impressed that it plans to buy 40,000 zero polluting taxis to replace the gasoline and diesel taxis in Mexico City. Mexico City suffers from the worst urban air pollution in the world. (A visionary plan for safe and low polluting urban transport is outlined in the chapter 'The Ultimate Safe and Efficient Traffic System', see page 207).

There are technological developments in agriculture that hold the promise of reducing chemical treatments by ninety per cent. Other technological developments are aimed at using natural biological systems to treat industrial effluent in an environmentally friendly way.

But a 'technological fix' alone will not solve our environmental problems. We must accept that we cannot have unlimited growth in a limited world. We must realise that happiness does not depend on infinite consumption. We can choose to live happily and healthily in a technological world by changing our lifestyles a bit and by developing sustainable technologies—or we can continue to feed on the world in the manner of a Roman orgy. Whichever option we choose will produce the result we deserve.

Does the Enhanced Greenhouse Effect Threaten our Future?

The world is warming up. It is widely assumed that we understand the causes, that the warming will have catastrophic consequences unless it is halted, and that we must immediately start to tackle this problem. However, when the facts are examined closely, it seems there may be less justification than one might think for making some of these assumptions. This argument is summarised by Robert C. Balling Jnr in *The True State of The Planet* (The Free Press, 1995).

The Earth and the Moon are the same distance from the Sun and each receives the same amount of heat per square metre of surface. The average surface temperature of the Earth is 15ºC and the average surface temperature of the Moon is −18ºC. The temperature difference is explained by the Earth's atmosphere—the blanket of gases that surrounds our planet and produces the greenhouse effect. The Moon has no atmosphere.

The greenhouse effect works as follows. The Sun radiates energy substantially as visible light of wavelength 0.4–0.7 micrometres (millionths of a metre). Our atmosphere is transparent to visible light and to the shortest wavelength infrared radiation from the Sun which reaches and heats the surface of the Earth. The Earth radiates the heat energy back into the atmosphere in the form of longer wavelength (4–100 micrometre) infrared radiation. Some of this outgoing infrared radiation is absorbed in the atmosphere. Water vapour and carbon dioxide (CO_2), normal constituents of the atmosphere, strongly absorb infrared radiation. This warms the lower atmosphere and keeps the Earth's surface hotter than it would otherwise be. Increasing the concentration of greenhouse gases intensifies the warming effect. Since 1850, human activities (mainly burning fossil fuel and deforestation) have increased the atmospheric concentration of CO_2 by twenty-five per cent—from about 285 parts per million (ppm) to 356 ppm.

Over the past one hundred years, many other gases that produce greenhouse warming have also been added to the atmosphere. Methane concentration has increased from 0.75 ppm in 1800 to 1.7 ppm today, mainly due to agricultural activities (principally from rice paddies and farting cattle). Nitrous oxide concentration has increased from 285 parts per billion (ppb) in 1850 to 310 ppb in 1990. Chloroflourocarbons (CFCs) are also being released to the atmosphere in low concentration but they are powerful greenhouse gases.

The overall effect of the several greenhouse gases may be approximated by calculating the 'equivalent carbon dioxide' value, i.e. how much CO_2 alone would be required to produce the same effect as all the greenhouse gases found in the atmosphere. Equivalent CO_2 levels increased from about 290 ppm in 1850 to 440 ppm in 1994.

Many scientists predict that the equivalent CO_2 value will double by the middle of the next century, compared to 1850 values. Scientists use computer models of the atmosphere to predict the resulting climate changes. These complex models push the largest computers to the limit. Despite efforts to date, however, many scientists admit that their models are still fairly primitive. It is also sensible to be wary of weather predictions for the year 2100 considering the known unreliability of weather predictions for next week.

A global warming is now predicted by the year 2100 by an amount in the range 1°C to 3.5°C, with a 'best' estimate of about 2°C. A 2°C warming would raise sea levels by about fifty centimetres over 1850 levels and this would place about ten million people at risk from flooding. The models also predict increased global rainfall, but soil moisture levels will decrease in many areas as the warming will increase evaporation. Climate predictions about wildfires, droughts and storms are also derived from the model results.

According to Balling, the models contain many weaknesses. For example, the role of oceans in absorbing CO_2 and storing and transporting heat is not adequately included. Also, clouds play a vital role in maintaining the energy balance of the Earth and cloud factors are particularly questionable in the models. The models don't adequately handle the effect of non-greenhouse gases that are also being added to the atmosphere and that have strong local and regional cooling effects. The models are improving all the time but the outputs from future models may look different from today's results.

Measurements have shown that the mean annual temperature of the Earth has increased by 0.54ºC since 1881, and we know that equivalent CO_2 levels rose by forty per cent over that period. When the warming trend is analysed, it is noted that nearly seventy per cent of the warming occurred in the first half of the record, while the bulk of the greenhouse gas build-up clearly occurred in the second half of the record. An obvious test of the computer models is to see if they can accurately simulate the observed temperature rise since 1881 when the forty per cent CO_2 increase is factored in. Until very recently the computer models were off by a factor of two, concluding that we should have had a warming of at least 1ºC over the period 1881 to 1993.

But is the observed increase in temperature of 0.54ºC over the last one hundred years really attributable to increased greenhouse gas emissions? Balling argues that factors such as volcanic dust in the atmosphere and the effects of a variable Sun can account for much of the temperature increase. Furthermore, satellite based, lower atmosphere monthly temperature measurements are available for the period 1979 to the present. These data reveal a cooling of 0.13ºC over this period. However, it was only recently realised that the satellite measurements were not corrected for the fact that the satellites are slowly falling back to Earth. The application of these corrections will probably eliminate the previously measured cooling effect.

Measures have been proposed to restrict greenhouse gas emissions, including moving to lower carbon-based fuels, improving energy efficiency and reversing deforestation. But Balling argues that even with these controls in place, the models still predict sixty-five per cent of the temperature increase that would occur in the absence of controls.

Balling presents enough evidence to demonstrate that much that has been said about the enhanced greenhouse effect is overstated.

However, his bottom line appears to be that until we know more, we should say little and we should refrain from taking action because it will be ineffectual. I cannot agree, as CO_2 and other greenhouse gases are building up in the atmosphere and the world is warming up. At least some of this warming is attributable to the greenhouse gases and probably more of it than Balling suspects—remember the satellite temperature data. Therefore, let us take measures to reverse the build-up of greenhouse gases, but let us stop waving placards declaring 'The End is Nigh'.

The Ultimate Safe and Efficient Traffic System

Everyone knows there is something radically wrong with the way we organise traffic—the results are accidents, gridlock, air pollution, wasted fuel and frayed tempers. There must be a better way. John Gilmore, Lecturer in Environmental Engineering at Dundalk Institute of Technology, has conceived of a radical and comprehensive solution. This chapter is based on his analysis.

The motor car is slightly over one hundred years old. So far, motor car accidents have killed more than twenty-five million people and have injured and disabled six hundred million people. In Ireland over four hundred people die annually on the roads and more than twenty are permanently consigned to wheelchairs. Road accidents also cost an enormous amount of money—£886 million in Ireland in 1997.

The combustion of petrol in the motor car produces carbon dioxide (CO_2) and water. Every car produces four times its weight in CO_2 per year. The build-up of CO_2 in the atmosphere is causing the world to warm up and cars contribute twenty per cent of global CO_2 emissions.

Petroleum is a fossil fuel, a limited precious resource. We are burning the Earth's fossil fuel 100,000 times faster than it is being replenished. Almost all petrol burned by motor cars can be considered to be wasted. The average weight of a saloon car is one tonne (1,000 kg). The average weight of an occupant is less than 100 kg, so ninety per cent of the fuel is used to move the car and only ten per cent to move the occupant. Because of various inefficiencies, only ten per cent of the fuel is used productively to overcome drag, which means that only one per cent of the fuel is used to carry the passenger—and ninety-nine is wasted.

The average efficiency of motor cars in developed countries is around

35 mpg (miles per gallon). We could do one hundred times better. The world record for a one-seater 'car' is 9,436 mpg. These cars are lightweight and small engined (30–50 cc). Small engines can still perform—a 250 cc Kart can sprint from 0–60 mph in 3 seconds, whereas a Porsche 911 takes 4.5 seconds. Even a 50 cc motor bike can reach 60 mph.

Traffic accidents are largely the result of human error so the ultimate solution is to remove human control of the driving process, replacing it with mechanical and electronic automation. This system could also vastly improve fuel efficiency and reduce pollution to an irreducible minimum.

John Gilmore's solution is a comprehensive network of channels along which lightweight cars travel. All driving, cornering, braking, etc. is effected by the channel itself. The passenger merely enters the system, keys in the desired destination and relaxes until arrival. The system would be designed to take maximum advantage of gravity to help move the cars just as gravity assists water transport through pipes. The system would have a siding on every street to allow embarkation and disembarkation. Vehicles would be well spaced apart and automatically controlled so that collisions could not occur. Traffic would move continuously—there would be no traffic lights. The small size and lightness of the cars would make for great fuel efficiency and very low pollution.

The system can be pictured as a staid version of a roller-coaster ride. Roller-coaster cars are mechanically lifted to a height and then released along a rail. The motive power from there to the end of the ride is natural gravity. The car is guided and banked by the guiding rail. These systems, despite being deliberately designed to thrill and scare, are very safe.

On first encounter, John Gilmore's vision has an uncomfortable aura of Brave New World. This reaction passes as the benefits and uncompromising logic of the system sink in. Nevertheless, one might argue that the proposed system is inflexible. With the channel system you could not travel exactly from A to B. You might have to walk a street length from A to board the system and walk another street length at the other end to reach B. But isn't this exactly what you have to do in Dublin now with the parking situation? In Gilmore's system the journey between the two short walks would be safe, quick, relaxing and non-polluting. At present the journey is dangerous, slow, stressful and dirty.

Gilmore also has proposals on the best way to transport goods. Most goods we use are small (packets of cornflakes, etc.) and are transported by lorry from factory to supermarket, packed into larger boxes. Ninety nine per cent of energy expended in this movement is wasted, as are vast volumes of packaging. Gilmore suggests that the best way to transport these goods is by pipeline. The Royal Mail in London does just this, beating London's gridlock by using a dedicated tunnel. Alternatively, the traffic channels, as previously described, which are empty at night, could be used.

John Gilmore recognises that his vision is radical, expensive to install and unlikely to be adopted in the near future. He suggests an alternative solution in the meantime. Personal motoring in cities could be confined to specially designed, lightweight cars that would move very economically at about 150 mpg. Traffic would move continuously along one-way streets and roundabouts at a speed limit of 15–20 mph. The car would be so light and of such a design (something like Motaball) that even if it hit a pedestrian no harm would ensue. If society insisted on retaining an option to travel faster than 15–20 mph, this faster traffic would be confined to a separate channel system.

It is all too easy to dismiss a vision such as John Gilmore's as interesting but impractical. But it already exists underneath airports, where baggage handling systems flow freely and efficiently. As a biochemist I am certainly no expert on traffic but, while I cannot evaluate John Gilmore's plan in a professionally critical manner, I know that the solution requires such radical and creative thinking. Gilmore is writing a book (*The Last Traffic Accident*) on his solution to the traffic problem.

A Day in the Life of a Health-Conscious Environmentalist

The day started off badly. I awoke from a fitful sleep about 7.00 am and noted with annoyance that my bedroom window was tightly closed. This meant that, all night long, I had been inhaling unnecessarily high concentrations of radon, the naturally occurring radioactive gas of which Cork has more than its fair share.

Grim-faced I arose, washed, dressed and went downstairs for breakfast. Naturally I eat 'healthy' food and breakfast consisted of pure orange juice, high fibre cereal and some toast on which I put a low-fat spread. As I ate, I read the information printed on the low-fat spread container and on the cereal box. The low-fat spread puzzled me. The spread has substantial body to it, despite the fact that, according to the information on the box, it is composed of little or nothing. The cereal box proudly and brashly proclaimed that an average serving of its contents contains the same amount of fibre as fifteen potatoes. For some reason I found this information more unsettling than reassuring.

After breakfast I drove to work. I always feel guilty about driving the car. It burns up precious oil resources and the exhaust gases are polluting. I should really use my bicycle but work is six miles away and it is all uphill on the way home. I am too soft. As I sit into the car a guilty secret flashes into my mind. The car is old and I never had it converted to run on lead-free petrol. I hope nobody knows this.

It was a lovely sunny day, without a cloud in the sky. This cheered me up for a few minutes until I remembered the depleted ozone layer high up in our atmosphere. This means that dangerous ultraviolet light from the sun is inadequately filtered out. Dangerous sunlight was pouring through the car's sunroof onto the top of my head, parts of which are not as generously covered as they once were. I inclined my head at an unnatural angle in order to avoid the sunlight. Drivers of oncoming cars noted my pose with quickened interest.

Into the office, where first of all I sat down to work on my personal computer. I like to get such work done first thing in the morning when I am fresh, as I find it tiring to work on this machine at arm's length later in the day. It is necessary to work at this distance from the machine in order to minimise the risk of exposure to magnetic emissions.

Midmorning coffee-break posed a dilemma. I have two jars of coffee in my office—one is decaffeinated and the other is not. I have seen reports which claim that caffeine is not good for you and, as a result, I normally drink decaffeinated coffee. The ordinary coffee is kept, like a bottle of whiskey, for special occasions. However, that morning I had heard a report on the radio to the effect that decaffeinated coffee is actually worse for your health than ordinary coffee. I decided to skip coffee altogether and, instead, drank a glass of milk. I hoped the milk didn't come from a 'mad cow'.

Lunch time arrived and off I went to the staff restaurant. The menu offered two choices—fish and pizza. The fish looked very appetising but, naturally, I had to check on its origin. I asked the woman who was serving if she knew where the fish was caught. She said she didn't but added that several customers had commented on how nice the fish tasted. I asked if she could specifically rule out an Irish Sea origin for the fish. She replied that for all she knew the fish might have been caught in the Dead Sea. I started to explain about radioactivity in the Irish Sea but had to cut it short when some colleagues in the queue behind me began to direct unnecessarily abusive language in my direction. I settled for a salad sandwich and a bottle of mineral water (the 'light' variety).

That evening, after a high fibre and low cholesterol tea, I sat down in my living room to relax and read the newspaper. After about half an hour we all agreed that there was a 'nip' in the air and my wife said that she would switch on the oil central heating. I suggested that we should postpone using the central heating until the weather became bitterly cold later in the year. I pointed out that oil was a scarce resource which should be conserved, that burning it contributed to the enhanced greenhouse effect and that we should compensate for the 'nip' in the air by wearing extra clothes. My wife retorted sharply that normal people remove rather than don their overcoats on entering a house. I appealed to the children who could see no merit in my argument except that it was very funny. On went the central heating. I sank into my armchair and guiltily brooded over a question that frequently pops into my mind—how had I built a house and not put even a single solar panel on it?

I switched on the television looking for some light entertainment. I only have two channels. Channel one was showing the news and channel two a documentary on the destruction of the tropical rainforests. No joy here. My eye wandered around the living room—teak skirting board, teak architrave and teak door. My God, how many scarce hardwood trees were destroyed in order to put wood into my house?

I decided to relax with a couple of beers before going to bed, so out came the six-pack. I was almost finished my second bottle but didn't feel any cheerier. What sort of beer was it anyway? I peered closely at the label—alcohol-free!

Time for bed. Up the stairs, cleaned the teeth, into the pyjamas and into bed, forgetting to crack the window open. As Buddha sagely pointed out a long time ago—'life is difficult'.

Science and Religion

Can Biology Explain Religion?

The central organising principle of modern biology is the Theory of Evolution. Biological scientists attempt to explain all aspects of the biological world in terms of evolutionary concepts. Without this theory, the vast assemblage of knowledge that has been accumulated about the biological world would simply represent an incoherent jumble of data.

The practice of religion has always been widespread in the world and dates back to ancient times. Actions based on religious motivations have played a major part in world history. It is important, therefore, to try to understand the basic reasons that impel human nature towards religious belief. The thinking of biologists on the matter is interesting but, in my opinion, still at an early stage of development.

The scientific method is competent to investigate and understand the natural mechanisms that apply in the natural world. I do not believe that the method is competent to answer other large questions—such as does God exist and does consciousness survive death? Science can only provide natural explanations. In many cases natural explanations are the complete explanations, but in other cases they may not be, and religion is one such example. In this chapter I will only consider natural explanation but, in so doing, I don't wish to give the impression that I am dismissive of other dimensions such as religious faith and theological studies.

Natural selection is the mechanism by which evolution works. Natural selection (the 'survival of the fittest') means that in each generation those individuals best suited to their environment survive and reproduce more efficiently than individuals less suited to the environment. In an evolutionary context, all characteristics of an organism, including the human pre-disposition to religion, are viewed as having survived because they conferred an advantage on the organism, and these characteristics are passed on genetically from one generation to the next. So, the question that biologists ask with regard to religion is: how does religion confer an advantage on humans that enhances survival and reproduction?

In a book published in 1984, *The Biology of Religion* by V. Reynolds and R. Tanner (Longman), the authors ranked the world's religions in the order in which they encourage reproduction—Islam, Hinduism, Judaism, Buddhism, Roman Catholicism and Protestantism. The authors say that this ranking would be roughly reversed if it were performed on the basis of gross national product in countries where these religions predominate. In poor subsistence–agrarian societies, there is pressure on couples to have considerable numbers of children in order to supply workers for the field and to ensure that there will be someone to look after the parents in old age. In the richer countries, survival and reproduction are not in question and the goal to be pursued is quality of life. There is no pressure here to have large numbers of children—in fact there is pressure to limit the number of children per couple.

The authors conclude that the biological imperative to develop appropriate reproductive strategies determines the religious preferences of people on a large-scale regional basis. But while this is an interesting conjecture regarding religious preferences, it does not address the root question as to the biological basis of religion per se. The immediate factors that determine the pressure to reproduce are economic, social and political. The correlation noted with type of religion practised may merely mean that general economic and social pressures are reflected in religious practices. Such correlation will also hold true for many other practices, such as types of sport, music, etc. Despite its bold title, this book by Reynolds and Tanner does not explain the biological basis of religion.

If there is a genetic basis for the human impulse towards religion, it must have a biochemical expression in the body. It is well-known, for example, that our emotions have a physiological or biochemical basis. The involuntary stomach-churning fear, experienced when we suddenly encounter a threat, is caused by a cascade of hormones released in the body that physiologically prepare us to either fight or flee. There is also a class of chemicals in the brain called the endorphins. These have a natural opiate-like action and, when released, cause enhanced feelings of contentment and also help us to cope better with pain. The general conclusion regarding a genetic predisposition towards religion, then, would be that we are genetically or biochemically 'wired' in a manner that causes us to feel good when we entertain religious feelings.

There are many problems associated with the human condition and a significant one is the question of why we exist. Are we purely the result of physical and chemical laws, allied to probability? When we die is consciousness extinguished? Or, on the other hand, is our existence part of a grand scheme governed by a good intelligence, with consciousness surviving bodily death? Obviously, the second scenario is vastly more pleasant to contemplate than the first. I am always surprised by people who tell me that they have calmly accepted the first scenario—that when they die, every aspect of them vanishes for ever. If I were convinced along these lines, it would certainly bother me and I imagine that most people would feel the same way.

The human brain has the capacity for reflective thought. The question of why we exist cannot be avoided and, in the absence of objective proof of divine purpose, early humanity faced the problem that a majority of people might fall into stultifying depression while contemplating the futility of existence. If you are sitting in black mood, head in hands, you are unlikely to be motivated to sally forth to reproduce! Perhaps evolution solved this problem by genetically programming us with a pre-disposition to plump for optimistic and rosy scenarios, even when objective evidence does not exist to support these scenarios.

At the moment, attempts at biological explanation of religion are little more than thoughtful speculation. The speculation may turn out to be true, or partly true. Even if the biological speculation turns out to be entirely correct, this says nothing about whether or not the teachings of the great world religions are valid. It would merely mean that these teachings have a naturally receptive audience.

Traditionally science has attempted to answer the questions relating to the 'how' of the world—religion attempts to answer the questions relating to 'why'. These 'why' questions must be answered and therefore religion plays a vital role, even though, as history shows, at times very wrong things have been done in the name of religion. But we also had two large-scale attempts this century to organise society without any input from religion. Both attempts were huge and tragic failures.

Science and Religion

Religion has been in decline for a considerable time in the West, while science has been growing and prospering. There is a widespread misconception that the two areas are fundamentally incompatible, i.e. that one cannot have both a truly scientific and a truly religious outlook. I do not accept this. As a scientist, I obviously believe in the value and the power of science. But I also believe in the value and power of a spiritual dimension. There has always been tension between science and religion and this will continue. I believe this tension is mutually beneficial. As Einstein said: 'Science without religion is lame, religion without science is blind'.

It is a basic characteristic of science that all scientific knowledge is revisable (that is, subject to revision) in the light of new compelling evidence. Newton worked out the basic physical laws of motion and gravity in the seventeenth century. Later, in the twentieth century, Einstein and others showed that Newton's laws apply precisely only to objects of the size we encounter in our everyday world and moving at speeds we are familiar with in the ordinary world. Modification must be introduced to describe movements of the very small (atoms) and the very large (astronomical), and movements at speeds approaching the speed of light.

Does science interpret Einstein's advance as a defeat of Newton's ideas and an embarrassment to science? Quite the contrary. Newton continues to be revered as possibly the greatest scientist of all time. Newton's main rival for that title is Einstein. Einstein's work is seen as enlarging and advancing on Newton's work, providing us with a glorious new vision. Science is full of examples where new research corrects, expands or completely overthrows older ideas. All such changes are seen as victories for science, not defeats. In this regard, religion should take a leaf out of science's book.

Humankind has always sought to know God and there seems little reason to doubt that this will always be true. Religion is the by-product of this search for God. In religion there are elements that are timeless, namely the principles as enunciated by the great teachers. Then there is the interpretation of the principles in terms of specific mechanisms and applications. This interpretation should be an evolving process that matures and sharpens as humankind develops. Religion keeps getting into trouble because of its reluctance to allow interpretations of principles to evolve in line with developments in scholarship, science and culture.

Take the Christian churches and evolution as an example. A literal interpretation of Genesis tells us that every species of life we know today was created separately by God. This was widely accepted by scientists and non-scientists alike until the announcement of the theory of evolution in 1858. The weight of the evidence produced by Darwin to show that species are not immutable, and that present species have slowly arisen from pre-existing species, was overwhelming.

The churches were shocked and staunchly resisted the new theory of evolution. However, in light of the body of evidence, the mainline churches gradually accommodated the new theory. The fundamentalist traditions staunchly reject evolution to this day. The mainline churches have a sufficiently rich intellectual tradition to accept evolution. The fundamentalist traditions, particularly American, stand largely bereft of an intellectual tradition and have beached themselves on the rocky shore of literalism.

Despite the fact that the mainline Christian churches largely accept evolution, this scientific advance is seen as a defeat for religion, not an advance—a defeat of magic by rationality. Even mainline religion subconsciously sees it in this light and is demoralised. In fact, quite a contrary view should be taken, along these lines: evolution shows that the story in Genesis is not to be taken literally and should be studied for its moral and symbolic meaning. In doing this, science has rendered the Judaeo–Christian tradition a great service.

Let us return to the overall scheme of timeless principle and understanding of specifics as it applies to the case of evolution. The principle is that the world exists and operates by the will of God. The interpretation of principle is our understanding at any given time of how the world works in concrete and specific terms. Prior to the theory of evolution, the interpretation regarding the biological world was that God created each species separately in an immutable form. After evolution our understanding is that God's scheme allows species to arise and evolve in a natural fashion. The understanding changed, the principle remains.

So, if Genesis is to be seen purely as a story bearing a moral message, what does this message mean? The first book of Genesis, in summary, tells the following story. God first created light and *saw it was good*. He then created land and *saw it was good*. He then separated the land and water and *saw it was good*. And so he created the plants and animals and, *seeing they were good*, he went on to create human beings. M. Scott Peck makes some interesting suggestions as to the moral messages in Genesis in his book *Further Along the Road Less Travelled* (Pocket Books, 1997). Peck suggests that at least part of the moral of the first book of Genesis is that creativity is intimately connected with the impulse to do good.

The third book of Genesis tells the story of Adam and Eve in the Garden of Eden. This can be interpreted as a description of the evolution of consciousness. With the evolution of consciousness and self-consciousness came a sense of separation from nature, shyness and, most importantly, the awareness of good and evil and consequent choice. Only when we became conscious were we faced with the choice of choosing the truth or the lie. Good and evil sprang into existence, since without choice you cannot have evil. Gone was the cosy unconscious security of the Garden of Eden. From now on humans prospered or withered as a consequence of consciously choosing good or evil.

Is Science Replacing Religion?

Richard Dawkins, the well-known writer on evolution, was recently in Ireland promoting his book, *Unweaving the Rainbow* (Penguin, 1998). He claimed in a radio interview that science is replacing religion and said: 'Science has nothing to learn from religion, and neither does anyone else'. Dawkins does science a disservice by promoting this idea. Obviously, if science takes over from religion, this will be bad for religion. But I believe it will also be bad for science. Science and religion have different functions and neither should stray beyond its function.

The function of science is to discover how the physical and material world works, using natural methods. Science is very powerful and successful, but is limited in scope. Science can answer only certain types of question. The sort of questions science can answer are (a) how does the world work? and (b) what consequence will result if a certain manipulation is carried out on a particular part of the world?

There are many types of question that science alone cannot answer. For example, science has accumulated a vast body of knowledge about the world. Much of this knowledge can be applied to do useful things (technology). It can also be used for bad ends. Science cannot tell us which are good applications and which are bad; which are better and which are worse; which we will like and which we will dislike (although it can help us to answer these questions). Science cannot devise codes of ethics and morality. By and large, science cannot tell us what will make us happy. And, by definition, science has nothing to say about the spiritual dimension.

The philosophy of materialism holds that nothing exists except matter and that the properties of matter explain all phenomena in the universe. A materialist cannot believe in God. It is not necessary to be a materialist to be a scientist. Many scientists are materialists, many are not. It is not necessary to be an atheist to be a scientist. Some scientists are atheists, many are not.

Science deals only with the natural world—the world of the material. But a scientist can study the natural world without denying that a supernatural realm also exists. Of course, the scientist must explain the natural world by natural mechanisms and cannot import a supernatural explanation into science.

Scientists who are also materialists feel that science has the potential to answer just about everything. They will not agree with me about the types of question that science cannot answer. They will feel that even if science cannot answer these questions at the moment, future advances will provide the answers. Many popular science writers are materialists (for example Peter Atkins, Stephen Rose and Richard Dawkins), which leads them to make very large claims for science. But only time will tell if science has any power to handle the types of question that seem to be, in my opinion, beyond its competence.

One function of religion is to answer questions like: what is the purpose of life? Another function of religion is to help us to lead moral lives. Science can tell us how we got to where we are today as biological organisms, and it can predict where we are going in the biological sense. But science cannot tell us if there is a purpose to our existence and where we might be going in that sense.

Questions about the purpose of life and about a supernatural realm existing independently of the body have always preoccupied the human mind. Religion provides a comprehensive answer for very many people. If religion were abolished, these questions would remain. Science cannot provide answers, but there is no shortage of primitive superstitions and magic to fill the vacuum. From a utilitarian perspective alone, mainstream religion plays a very useful role.

In pre-scientific times, religion not only answered the question of the purpose of life, but it also explained various parts of the natural world. Thus, for example, we have the Genesis creation account in the Bible and, later, the Church endorsing the Earth-centred structure of the universe. Neither of these interpretations stand up against the alternative explanations provided by science. The Church has long since accepted the scientific description of the structure of the universe and mainstream Christian traditions are now happy to accept Genesis as a story rather than as a literal account.

In the past the Church at times bitterly opposed science, but no longer. But new and powerful opponents of science have emerged. These include an assortment of New Age philosophies and, surprisingly, bitter criticism from social sciences and the humanities. Science should concentrate on its new critics and not waste energy poking an old dog that no longer barks at it.

Dawkins is correct in a limited sense to claim that science is taking over from religion—but only in the sense that the Church cedes the ground where science can show that a particular part of the natural world works differently from an explanation previously provided by the Church. In deferring to science in this manner, religion loses none of its essence, which is to explain the purpose of life. The essence of science is to explain the natural world. Each to its own.

I think science is great. But there are many other things in the world that are great—family, love, friendship, literature, music, art and natural beauty, for example. And, of course, religion. Bryan Appleyard, in his powerful book *Understanding the Present* (Pan Books, 1992), charges that science is unable to co-exist with other values and, in the long run, takes over the niches that have been occupied by these values. He likens science to a crocodile, unable to turn its head and only able to move forward blindly with all-devouring jaws. I do not accept this but I cringe when I hear some of the florid pronouncements of popular science writers. By all means let us advance in science, but let us make haste with some humility.

God and Science

Bertrand Russell, the famous British mathematician and philosopher, did not believe in God. He was once asked by a woman: 'Mr Russell, you don't believe in God, but what will you do if, after you die, you unexpectedly find yourself rushed before the throne of God for judgement?' Russell replied: 'In that case, Madam, I will be happy to change my mind.'

As a science columnist I have been struck by the number of correspondents, over the years, who automatically assume that I don't believe in God. Is it possible to be a scientist and to believe in God? The answer is yes. There are innumerable examples of eminent scientists, both past and present, who believe in God. I am a scientist and I am also a Christian.

What do I mean by believing in God? I mean belief in a supreme being of infinite knowledge, wisdom and goodness, by whose will the world exists. Christians believe that human nature somehow reflects the image of God and that our purpose is to develop this nature so that we can approximate better to the divine image. (I have no competence to discuss other than the Christian concept of God.)

Science is the study of the natural mechanisms that underpin the natural world and, as such, it has nothing to say about the existence of God. Scientists are free to hold such beliefs about God as their wits, as whole human beings, can construe for them.

God is not self-evident from a study of the natural details of the world and there is no evidence that God's ongoing intervention is necessary in order to keep the world working. It seems to me that God's existence can never be 'provable'. If it could, then all but the insane would be bound to believe and that would remove our freedom of choice to accept or reject God. It is much more likely that we are supplied with just enough evidence to allow us to reasonably conclude that God exists, but only if we apprehend this evidence with all our faculties.

The philosophy of materialism holds that the material structure of the universe explains all phenomena that exist. Many people think that a scientist must also be a materialist. This is not true. Many scientists are materialists, many are not. Many prominent scientists in the past have either had a straightforward belief in the Christian concept of God, or else have accepted the existence of some form of supreme supernatural creative intelligence. These scientists include Isaac Newton, James Clerk Maxwell, Charles Darwin, Max Plank, Werner Heisenberg, George Boole and Albert Einstein.

Probably the single greatest thing about the natural world is that it is understandable and its laws can be stated mathematically. Einstein had a deep reverence for the rational nature of reality. He declared:

> Certain it is that the conviction, akin to religious feelings, of the rationality or intelligibility of the world lies behind all scientific work of a higher order . . . this firm belief, a belief bound up with deep feeling, in a superior mind that reveals itself in the world of experience, represents my conception of God.

He also said: 'I want to know how God created this world. I want to know His thoughts, the rest are details.'

Neither is there any shortage today of eminent scientists who believe in God. The book *Cosmos, Bios, Theos* (edited by H. Margenau and R. A. Varghese, Open Court, 1992) is a collection of interviews with sixty prominent scientists, many of them Nobel Prize winners. Thirty-seven of these scientists profess an unambiguous belief in God.

Humanism is a widespread western alternative to religion. It denies the existence of any power or moral value superior to humanity and rejects religion in favour of a belief that humanity can advance itself by its own efforts. The humanist believes that human beings are the product of blind evolutionary forces and that conceptions of God are merely delusions that flicker through the brains of many. Humanists do not believe that humans arose for any particular purpose. The humanist believes that when a person dies that is the end of him or her. They also believe that in five billion years' time, when our Sun dies, that will be the end for humanity.

The humanist vision is tragic in at least two senses. One relates to the limited prospects for developing human capacities and the other to the irredeemable nature of human suffering. Human beings have the unique capacity to grow in wisdom, knowledge, self-awareness and love. In principle there would seem to be no limit to the development of these valuable aspects of human nature. But if the humanist philosophy is true, these aspirations can only be fulfilled in a very limited and temporary fashion. Such aspirations would be appropriate to beings made for eternal life in a universe designed for the development of personal values.

Human suffering is widespread. Even today, a majority of people on the planet live under conditions of abject poverty, malnourishment and disease. Over ages past, the sum total of human anguish and pain that has been endured beggars the power of the imagination. According to humanism, the suffering of the innocent in this life is just an unfortunate fact—it is irredeemable. On the other hand, Christianity views life in relation to a divine purpose of love and sees how, out of suffering, can come a good of infinite value—a good which justifies the pain of the suffering.

Because certain aspects of the vision offered by humanism are unpalatable, it does not mean that the philosophy must be untrue. However, it seems to me that, since the God hypothesis can answer the tragic aspects of the humanist philosophy so comfortably, it should at least be carefully considered by all.

On the other hand, while it may well be comforting to believe in the existence of God, is such a belief reasonable or is it just a comforting illusion? After all, there is no logical or scientific proof that God exists. A belief that is reasonable simply means that there are adequate grounds for the belief. Are there adequate grounds for belief in God? I believe that for some people there are adequate grounds and for others there aren't.

Belief in the Christian God centres on our response to the life and the teaching of Jesus Christ. Did Jesus himself have adequate grounds for belief in God? It is clear from the gospel that Jesus believed with every fibre of his being that he lived in the presence of God, with whom he had easy and open communication. For Jesus not to believe in God would have been to reject his own sanity. So, what about the reasonableness of our belief in God? If we find that the teachings of Jesus strike a deep chord in us and stake a claim on our hearts and minds; if the words of Jesus strike us as coming from a cool and sane mind; if following the teaching of Jesus produces positive effects in our lives, then I believe we have adequate grounds for belief in the God of whom Jesus spoke. On the other hand, if a person finds that he or she cannot respond positively in these ways, then such a person does not have adequate grounds for belief in God.

As a scientist I am proud of the spectacular progress that science has made over the past several hundred years in advancing our understanding of the natural world. And there is no reason to think that this progress will not continue indefinitely. But there is more to understanding the world in its entirety than science alone can command, powerful as it is. I believe that the appropriate way to approach such a large question as the existence of God is by the apprehension of the world with all our human senses—that is by using our wisdom gained from experience, our intuition, our capacity to love and our emotions, in addition to our analytical minds. If the question is approached exclusively through logical scientific analysis one will probably come to the same conclusion as Bertrand Russell.

Notes on Some of the Scientists Referred to in the Text

Henri Becquerel (1852–1908)

French physicist who discovered the first indication of radioactivity in the form of penetrating radiation coming from uranium salts. He shared the 1903 Nobel Prize in Physics with Marie and Pierre Curie. Becquerel subsequently showed that radioactivity of radium consists of a stream of electrons.

Ludwig Boltzmann (1844–1906)

Austrian physicist who explained the properties of gases in terms of the motion of their constituent atoms and molecules, the kinetic theory of gases. He founded a branch of physics known as statistical mechanics. He derived a formula called the Boltzmann Distribution which calculates the number of atoms or molecules with a given energy at a particular temperature. Boltzmann became depressed by opposition to some of his theories and committed suicide shortly before his ideas became widely accepted.

Louis de Broglie (1892–1987)

French theoretical physicist who established that all subatomic particles can be described either by equations that treat them as particles or as waves— the wave–particle duality of matter. He was awarded the 1929 Nobel Prize for Physics. His work allowed physicists to appreciate that Einstein's conviction that matter and energy are interconvertible is fundamental to the structure of matter. He worked from 1946 as senior adviser to the government on the development of atomic energy in France.

Rudolf Clausius (1822–1888)

German physicist and a founder of the science of thermodynamics; in 1850 he announced the second law of thermodynamics in the form 'heat cannot flow from a colder to a hotter body'. He concluded that entropy (disorder) must increase in the universe.

Nicolaus Copernicus (1473–1543)

Polish astronomer who opposed Christian doctrine at the time by declaring that the Sun, not the Earth, is at the centre of the solar system. Copernicus studied mathematics, law, medicine and astronomy at Krakow and at universities in Italy. Returning to Poland in 1506 he became physician to his uncle, a bishop, who appointed him as Canon at Frombork. Copernicus demoted the Earth from the centre of the universe to the status of a mere planet that revolves around the centre. This forced a revision of the prevailing anthropocentric view of the universe and delivered a grave shock to European culture.

Francis Crick (b. 1916)

English molecular biologist. He studied physics at University College London and later did biological research at Cambridge. He shared the 1962 Nobel Prize with Maurice Wilkins and James Watson for work on the molecular structure of DNA and the mechanism whereby characteristics are transferred from generation to generation. Crick and Watson proposed in 1953 that DNA is a double helix made of two chains of alternate sugar and phosphate groups and linked together by pairs of organic bases. Later Crick, with others, showed that each group of three adjacent bases on a single DNA strand codes for a specific amino acid. Proteins are composed of amino acids and the sequence of bases in DNA codes for the sequence of amino acids in protein. In 1977 Crick became a Professor at the Salk Institute, San Diego, California.

Charles Darwin (1809–1882)

English biologist who developed the theory of evolution and proposed, together with Alfred Russel Wallace, the principle of natural selection. Darwin studied medicine at Edinburgh and theology at Cambridge. He travelled to South America and the Galapagos Islands as naturalist on HMS *Beagle* 1831–36. He developed his ideas on evolution and natural selection on his return to England but did not publish them until 1858 when he was forced into action by receiving a memoir from Wallace describing the same theory. In 1859 Darwin published his now famous book whose full title is: *On the Origin of Species by Means of Natural Selection or the Preservation of Favoured Races in the Struggle for Life*. The book aroused much controversy because it disagreed with a literal interpretation of the Book of Genesis in the Bible. The Theory of Natural Selection notes the variations that exist between members of a sexually reproducing population. Those members with variations better suited to the environment are more likely to survive and breed, passing on these desirable characteristics to offspring. In 1871 Darwin published his book *The Descent of Man* in which he proposed that man is also descended from ape-like ancestors.

Richard Dawkins (b. 1941)

British zoologist who has written several best-selling books outlining the modern theory of evolution. His books include *The Selfish Gene* (1976), *The Blind Watchmaker* (1986) and *River Out of Eden* (1996). Dawkins believes that genes, not individuals, populations or species, are the driving force of evolution. He also believes that human culture is transmitted in an analogous way and coined the term 'meme' as the unit of such a scheme. Dawkins believes the idea of God is a meme. Dawkins is Professor of the Public Understanding of Science at Oxford University.

Albert Einstein (1879–1955)

German-born US physicist who formulated the Theories of Relativity and worked on radiation physics and on thermodynamics.

Einstein was born in Germany and lived in Italy and Switzerland where he became an inspector of patents, working on his PhD in his spare time. He taught at Zurich University and in 1913 became Director of the Kaiser Wilhelm Institute for Physics at Berlin. Deprived of his position by the Nazis he emigrated to America in 1933 where he spend the rest of his life.

Einstein received the Nobel Prize for Physics in 1921 in recognition of his work on the connection between the absorption of light by matter and the emission of electricity—the photoelectric effect. But he is best remembered for his Theories of Relativity.

The Special Theory of Relativity describes how the world appears to an observer moving at a steady velocity. This theory contains the famous equation $E=MC^2$, which states that energy and matter are interconvertible.

The General Theory of Relativity extended the Special Theory to include observers in accelerated frames of reference. This theory envisages the universe as permeated by a space–time continuum where properties are modified locally by the presence of matter. Light and material objects follow the contours of the continuum and consequently light rays bend when they pass by a massive object and a planet orbits around the Sun following its natural trajectory in modified space–time.

Galileo Galilei (1564–1642)

Italian mathematician, astronomer and physicist. He began the modern scientific revolution and founded the method of deducing laws to explain the results of observation and experiment.

Galileo developed the astronomical telescope and was the first to observe clearly the pock-marked surface of the Moon, sunspots, the satellites of Jupiter and the phases of Venus, thus proving it orbits the Sun. He discovered that all freely falling bodies (heavy or light) have the same constant acceleration and these bodies moving on horizontal perfectly smooth surfaces neither slow down or speed up.

Galileo was born in Pisa and became Professor of Mathematics at Pisa University in 1589. In 1610 he became Chief Mathematician to the Grand Duke of Tuscany.

Galileo's work was an unwelcome refutation of the Aristotelian ideas taught at the Church-run universities. For the first time his work made the theory of Nicolaus Copernicus plausible, i.e. that the sun sits at the centre of the solar system and the Earth revolves around it. Galileo's important book *Dialogues on the Two Chief Systems of The World* (1632) was banned by the Church and he was forced to recant his views by the Inquisition. After recantation he is reputed to have muttered: 'Eppur si muove' ('Yet it does move'). He spent his remaining years under house arrest.

George Gamow (1904–1968)

Russian-born cosmologist and nuclear physicist. His work included a study of the structure and evolution of stars and of the creation of the elements. He showed how nuclear fusion reactions could power the energy of the Sun, and, with others, he postulated the Big Bang Theory which indicated the origin of the universe. Gamow defected from Russia to America in the 1930s and became a Professor at George Washington University. He worked on the atomic bomb at Los Alamos, New Mexico, in the 1940s.

Stephen Jay Gould (b. 1941)

US palaeontologist and writer. His theory of punctuated equilibrium in 1972 proposes that evolution of species does not occur at a steady rate but can undergo accelerated change over a few hundred thousand years. He has written many popular books, including *Wonderful Life* (1990).

Edmund Halley (1656–1742)

British astronomer who became the second Royal Astronomer in 1720. In 1705 he identified the comet now known by his name. He calculated that cometary sightings reported in 1456, 1531, 1607 and 1682 all were reappearances of the same comet. He predicted the comet would reappear in 1758, which it did.

Halley also compiled a star catalogue and detected the proper motion of stars. He was a friend of Isaac Newton and financed the publication of Newton's great work *Principia*.

Stephen Hawking (b. 1942)

English physicist. He became Lucasian Professor of Mathematics at Cambridge in 1979, the same chair held by Newton. Hawking works in the field of general relativity and searches for a quantum theory of gravity to explain black holes and the Big Bang. His most notable discovery was that black holes (stars that have totally collapsed and whose gravity is so great that nothing, not even light, can escape from them) can in fact emit particles in the form of thermal radiation. His popular book *A Brief History of Time*

(1986), a simple account of cosmology, was an international best-seller.

Fred Hoyle (b. 1915)

English astronomer and cosmologist. His most significant work was to show, together with William Fowler in 1957, how chemical elements heavier than hydrogen and helium are built up by nuclear reactions inside stars. In 1948, with others, he formulated the Steady State Theory of the universe, now generally fallen out of popularity in favour of the Big Bang theory. Hoyle also proposes that life in the universe began in space in interstellar gas clouds and was seeded on Earth by comets. Hoyle has also written much science-fiction. His first science-fiction novel was *The Black Cloud* (1957).

Edwin Hubble (1889–1953)

US astronomer. He discovered the existence of galaxies beyond our own and classified them by shape. His theory that the universe is expanding is now generally accepted. He announced Hubble's Law in 1929 which says that galaxies are moving apart at a rate that increases with their distance. The ratio of the velocity of galactic recession to distance is called Hubble's Constant. Hubble worked at Mount Wilson Observatory, California, from 1914 onwards.

Christian Huygens (1629–1695)

Dutch mathematical physicist and astronomer. He made important advances in pure and applied mathematics and in mechanics. He developed the pendulum clock in 1657. Perhaps most famously, he proposed the wave theory of light.

William Thomson Kelvin (1824–1907)

Irish physicist. He introduced the absolute scale of temperature called the Kelvin Scale and his work on the conservation of energy (1851) led to the Second Law of Thermodynamics. Kelvin was born in Belfast and became Professor of Natural Philosophy at Glasgow University (1846–99) where he created the first physics laboratory in a UK university.

Johannes Kepler (1571–1630)

German mathematician and astronomer. He became assistant to Danish astronomer Tycho Brahe in 1600 and succeeded him as Imperial Mathematician to Holy Roman Emperor Rudolph II. Kepler formulated three Laws of Planetary Motion:

- The orbit of a planet is an elipse with the Sun at one of the foci.
- The radius from the planet to the Sun sweeps out equal areas on the ellipse in equal times.
- The squares of the periods (time of one complete revolution around the Sun) of planets are proportional to the cubes of their mean distance from the Sun.

James Clerk Maxwell (1831–1879)

Scottish physicist. Maxwell's most fundamental achievement was to bring the phenomena of electricity, magnetism and light together in one set of equations—Maxwell's Equations. He inferred that light consists of electromagnetic waves and suggested that light was only one member of a whole family of electromagnetic radiations. Maxwell also studied colour vision and showed how all the colours are built up from mixtures of the primary colours red, green and blue. He confirmed Thomas Young's theory that the eye has three types of receptors sensitive to the primary colours.

Gregor Mendel (1822–1884)

Austrian biologist and the founder of genetics. His observations of plant breeding experiments with peas led him to propose a theory of particulate inheritance (as opposed to blending) involving dominant and recessive characters. Mendel was an Augustinian monk. He published his results (1865–69) but they remained unappreciated until rediscovered at the turn of the century.

Albert Michelson (1852–1931)

German-born US physicist. In 1887, together with Edward Morley, he carried out the Michelson–Morley experiment to detect the motion of the Earth through the ether. The ether was a ghostly medium believed to permeate the universe and to be necessary for the propagation of light. The results of the experiment indicated the non-existence of the ether and showed that the velocity of light is constant whatever the motion of the observer. Michelson was awarded the Nobel Prize in Physics in 1907.

Walther Nernst (1864–1961)
German physical chemist. He won the 1920 Nobel Prize in Chemistry for work on heat changes in chemical reactions. In 1906 he proposed the Third Law of Thermodynamics—the entropy of a perfect crystal is zero at a temperature of absolute zero.

Isaac Newton (1642–1727)
English physicist who laid the foundations of modern physics and made cardinal discoveries in mathematics. In 1665–66 he discovered the calculus and showed that white light is composed of many colours. He formulated the three Laws of Motion and the Theory of Universal Gravitation.

n Newton's Laws of Motion are:

n Unless influenced by an unbalanced force, a body at rest remains at rest, and a body in motion continues moving in a straight line at the same speed.

n When an unbalanced force is applied to a body it will cause the body to accelerate in the direction of the force at a rate proportional to the force.

n When a body A exerts a force on a body B, B exerts an equal and opposite force on A.

Newton's Law of Universal Gravitation states that the gravitational force of attraction between any two bodies is proportional to the masses of the bodies and inversely proportional to the square of the distance between the bodies.

Newton published his great work in *Philosophica Naturalis Principia Mathematica* (1687). Newton showed that scientific principles have universal application. He calculated the motion of the Moon on the basis of his Theory of Gravity and he showed that his Theory of Gravity explained Kepler's Laws of Planetary Motion.

Newton was appointed Professor of Mathematics at Cambridge at the age of 26. He was appointed Warden of The Royal Mint in 1696. He spent the last thirty years of his life preoccupied with studies of theology, chronology and alchemy.

Louis Pasteur (1822–1895)

French chemist and microbiologist. He discovered that fermentation is caused by micro-organisms. Pasteur's careful investigations finally killed off the theory of the spontaneous generation of life from inanimate matter. He developed the germ theory of disease. Pasteur developed a vaccine for rabies and for other diseases. The process of pasteurisation—a gentle heating sufficient to kill off harmful or spoiling micro-organisms—is based on his discoveries. He headed the Pasteur Institute in Paris from 1888 to his death.

Ptolemy (Claudius Ptolemaeus) (c. AD100–c. AD170)

Egyptian astronomer and geographer. He worked in Alexandria. Ptolemy placed the Earth, a prefect sphere, at the centre of the universe. The planets revolved around the Earth in circular orbits but some of them orbited in epicycles, i.e. orbited a point that itself orbited the Earth. The sphere of the stars formed a dome with points of light attached. The Ptolemaic System was the standard astronomical map until the sixteenth century.

Wilhelm Roentgen (1845–1923)

German physicist. When he worked as Director of the Physical Institute at Wurzburg he discovered X-rays. The use of X-rays in medical diagnosis quickly revolutionised this field. He was awarded the Nobel Prize for Physics in 1901. He refused to take any financial gain out of his discovery believing that the fruits of scientific research should be fully available to all.

Harold Urey (1893–1981)

US chemist. In 1923 he discovered a heavy form of hydrogen called deuterium and he isolated heavy water. He was awarded the Nobel Prize for Chemistry in 1934. During the Second World War he worked on the Manhattan Project which produced the atomic bomb. In 1952 Urey proposed that molecules formed in the primitive atmosphere of the early Earth could have spontaneously combined to form life.

Alfred Russel Wallace (1823–1913)

Welsh naturalist. He collected plant and animal specimens in South America and Asia and independently formulated a theory of evolution by natural selection similar to the theory envisaged by Charles Darwin. Wallace told Darwin of his idea. Darwin had not yet published his theory. Darwin and Wallace together presented a paper to the Linnean Society in 1858 outlining their theory. Wallace disagreed with Darwin on the mechanism whereby human higher intelligence arose. He believed that the human physical form had evolved by natural selection but invoked some 'metabiological agency' to explain the emergence of human consciousness.

James Watson (b. 1928)

US biologist. His work with Francis Crick on the molecular structure of DNA and on the genetic code won him a shared Nobel Prize in 1962. From 1989 to 1992 he headed the US government's Human Genome Project.

Thomas Young (1773–1829)

British physicist, physician and Egyptologist. A child prodigy, he had learned most European languages and several ancient languages by the age of 20. He studied medicine and worked as a physician from 1811. Young revived the wave theory of light and produced conclusive evidence by identifying the phenomenon of interference. Interference is the interaction of two or more wave motions to produce waves of larger or smaller amplitude. Young carried out pioneering investigations of the focussing action of the eye and on the mechanism of colour perception by the eye. He established many important concepts in mechanics. He published many papers on Egyptology. His work on the Rosetta Stone played a critical role in the eventual decoding of the stone's message.

Source: *The Hutchinson Dictionary of Scientists* (Helicon Publishing Ltd 1996)

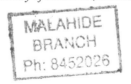

Recommended Further Reading

Recommended Further Reading

The Universe at Large and The Solar System

The Whole Shebang: A State-of-the-Universe Report Timothy Ferris
(Weidenfeld and Nicolson, 1997)

Almost Everyone's Guide to Science John Gribbin
(Weidenfeld and Nicolson, 1998)

Before the Beginning: Our Universe and Others Martin Rees
(Touchstone, 1998)

Cosmos Carl Sagan
(Abacus, 1995)

The Search for Extraterrestrial Intelligence: Listening for Life in the Cosmos
Thomas R. McDonough
(Wiley, 1987)

Creation Revisited: The Origin of Space, Time and the Universe Peter Atkins
(Penguin, 1994)

Laws of Physics

The Laws of Physics Isaac Asimov
(Barnes and Noble, 1993)

Fire in The Mind: Science, Faith and the Search for Order George Johnson
(Viking, 1996)

Was Einstein Right? C. Will
(Basic Books, 1986)

Subtle is The Lord A. Pais
(Oxford University Press, 1988)

Schrödinger's Kittens and the Search for Reality John Gribbin
(Weidenfeld and Nicolson, 1995)

'A Special Theory of Relativity' John Gribbin *New Scientist*
(*Inside Science*, No. 49), 21 September, 1991

'A Theory of Some Gravity' John Gribbin *New Scientist*
(*Inside Science*, No. 31), 24 February, 1990

The Origin of Life and The Theory of Evolution
The Fifth Miracle: The Search for the Origin of Life Paul Davies
(Penguin, 1998)
River out of Eden Richard Dawkins
(Weidenfeld and Nicolson, 1995)
Wonderful Life: The Burgess Shale and the Nature of History
Stephen Jay Gould
(Hutchinson Radius, 1989)
Lifelines Steven Rose
(Penguin, 1997)
Microcosmos: Four Billion Years of Microbial Evolution
Lynn Margulis and Dorian Sagan
(Allen and Unwin, 1987)
Darwin's Dangerous Idea: Evolution and the Meanings of Life.
Daniel C. Dennett
(Allen Lane, 1995)

Genetics, Medicine and Disease
The Language of the Genes Steve Jones
(Flamingo, 1993)
Genetic Engineering, Dreams and Nightmares Enzo Russo and David Love
(Oxford University Press, 1998)
Clone Gina Kolate
(Penguin, 1997)
Why We Age Steven N. Auslad
(Wiley, 1997)
*Cancer Wars: How Politics Shapes What We Know and Don't Know about
Cancer* Robert N. Proctor
(Basic Books 1995)
The Psychology of Health (2nd Edition)
Marian Pitts and Kiety Philips (Eds.)
(Routledge, 1998)

The Environment

Environmental Science – A Global Concern
William P. Cunningham and Barbara W. Saigo.
(Wm C. Brown, 1990)
Our Stolen Future Theo Colborn, John P. Myers and Dianne Dumanoski
(Little, Brown, 1996)
The True State of The Planet Ronald Bailey (ed.)
(The Free Press, 1995)
Radioactivity William Reville
(Briefing Sheet No. 7 – 3rd ed., ENFO, 17 St Andrew Street, Dublin 2)
Nuclear Radiation, Risks and Benefits Edward Pochin
(Oxford University Press, 1985)

Science and Religion

God, Chance and Necessity Keith Ward
(One World Publications, 1996)
God, Faith and The New Millennium: Christian Belief in an Age of Science
Keith Ward
(One World Publications, 1998)
Belief in God in an Age of Science John Polkinghorne
(Yale University Press, 1998)

Index

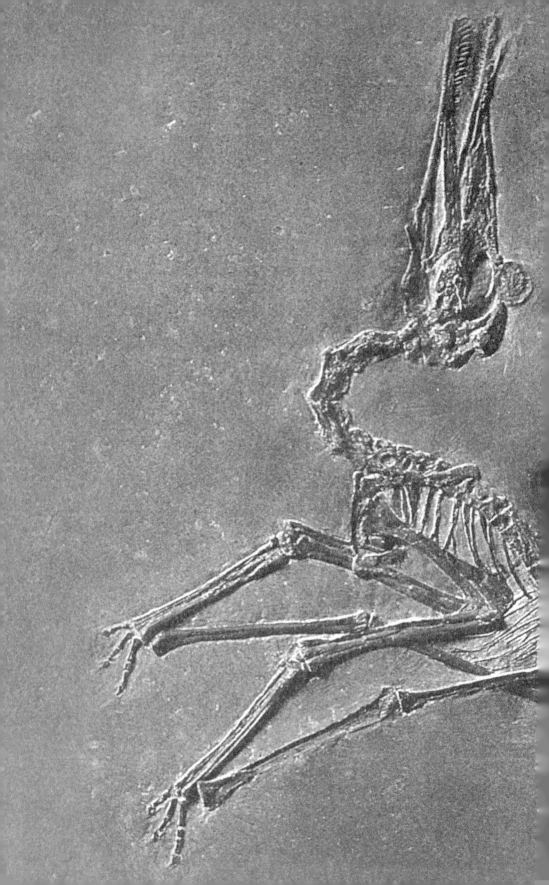